C000175190

Military Museums in the UK

A visitor's guide to over 140 museums in England, Scotland, Wales and Northern Ireland, produced by the Army Museums Ogilby Trust

Copyright © 2007 Army Museums Ogilby Trust

First published in 2007 by Third Millennium Publishing Limited,
a subsidiary of Third Millennium Information Limited,
2–5 Benjamin Street, London EC1M 5QL, United Kingdom

www.tmiltd.com

ISBN-13 978 1 903942 61 1
ISBN-10 1 903942 61 6

All rights reserved

No part of the contents of this book may be reproduced, stored in a retrieval
system, or transmitted in any form or by any means, electronic, mechanical,
photocopying, recording, or otherwise, without the written permission of
Third Millennium Publishing Limited.

Produced by Third Millennium Publishing,
a subsidiary of Third Millennium Information Limited

Designed by Matthew Wilson
Edited by Colin Sibun
Production by Bonnie Murray

Printed by 1010 Printing International Ltd
on behalf of Compass Press Ltd

Contents

Foreword

by

His Royal Highness The Duke of York KG, KCVO, ADC

BUCKINGHAM PALACE

Military museums across the country are a rich source of historical information and they provide unique insights into the inspirational deeds of courage, bravery and good humoured fortitude that have characterised the British Army through the centuries.

The Army Museums Ogilby Trust was established to safeguard the principal feature which its founder believed distinguished the British Army from all others, and that was the fighting spirit that its soldiers drew from the regimental system. At a time of change and reorganisation, when the identities of famous old regiments become blurred by amalgamation and new ones take their place, the museums described in this Guide ensure that the golden thread of Britain's military heritage is preserved for the Nation and made accessible to the public.

Regimental and Corps museums, together with the prestigious National museums also listed in this Guide, form a network that stretches throughout the United Kingdom. Often taking their character from the communities that provide their soldiers, they can impose a local perspective on their portrayal of events of national importance. In addition to the collections that are so proudly displayed, most of them possess valuable archive material and many provide modern, interactive displays to educate and entertain. They have something of interest for all from Old Comrades to the adventurous young and from the serious student of military history to the casual visitor.

As Patron of the Army Museums Ogilby Trust, I have no hesitation in warmly recommending a visit to each and every one of the museums in this Guide.

Introduction

This Guide, produced by the Army Museums Ogilby Trust
(AMOT), is the successor to the very popular publication
first compiled by Terence and Shirley Wise in 1969 and
revised periodically ever since. The Trust is most grateful
to the original authors for agreeing the transfer of
copyright and to Third Millennium Publishing without
whose generous support and expert professional help the
publication would not have been possible.

The Army Museums Ogilby Trust is a registered charity
founded in 1954 by Colonel Robert Ogilby to support and
promote the regimental and corps museums of the British
Army. This Guide is a natural extension of that role and
complements the Trust's website,
www.armymuseums.org.uk, which not only lists all the
museums but includes useful advice on ancestor research
and regimental bibliographies for genealogists and
military historians.

In Part I of the Guide, 136 regimental and corps museums
are listed alphabetically, by location, in 13 regional
sections, each with its own accompanying map. Part II
contains details of the principal national museums of

military interest and AMOT is grateful for their support.
Towards the back of the Guide is a Succession of Titles
containing a simple table which enables the reader to
trace the identity of a cavalry or infantry regiment from its
title in the 1881 Army List right through to the most
recent round of regimental amalgamations in 2006/7.

The final section provides more information about the
Army Museums Ogilby Trust, its founder, objectives and
activities in support of regimental and corps museums.
The Trust is a private charity which receives no
Government funding. Its income is derived solely from
donations and bequests and it would warmly welcome
gifts, legacies or covenants from those who support its
views and objectives. Information on how this may be
done is available at the back of the Guide.

Colin Sibun
Director
Army Museums Ogilby Trust
February 2007

WARNING

All details of opening hours and admission prices are correct at the time of publication but these do change from time to time and visitors are strongly encouraged to contact museums before making a visit

Part I

Regimental and Corps Museums

Listed alphabetically by location in the following Regional sections:

1 **South West England**

2 **The South of England**

3 **South East England**

4 **London**

5 **East Anglia**

6 **Wales**

7 **West Midlands**

8 **East Midlands**

9 **North West England**

10 **Yorkshire**

11 **North East England**

12 **Northern Ireland**

13 **Scotland**

South West

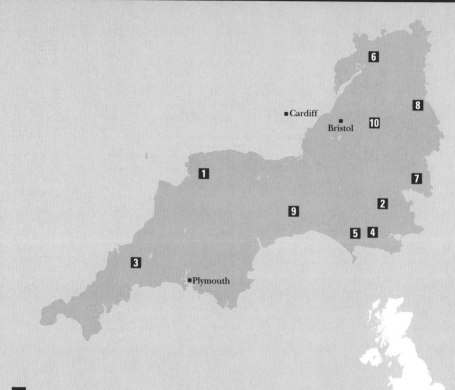

1	Barnstaple:	**Royal Devon Yeomanry**
2	Blandford Forum:	**Royal Signals Museum**
3	Bodmin:	**Duke of Cornwall's Light Infantry**
4	Bovington:	**The Tank Museum**
5	Dorchester:	**The Keep Military Museum**
6	Gloucester:	**Soldiers of Gloucestershire Museum**
7	Salisbury:	**Royal Gloucestershire, Berkshire & Wiltshire Regiment**
8	Swindon:	**Royal Wiltshire Yeomanry**
9	Taunton:	**Somerset Military Museum**
10	Warminster:	**Infantry and Small Arms School Corps Weapons Collection**

Barnstable

ROYAL DEVON YEOMANRY MUSEUM COLLECTION

Museum situated in the town centre near the clock tower on the square at the end of Long Bridge. A short walk from bus and railway stations. By road, follow signs to town centre from the North Devon Link Road

 Museum of Barnstaple and North Devon
The Square, Barnstaple,
Devonshire EX32 8LN
T: 01271 346747 F: 01271 346407
E: Alison.Mills@northdevon.gov.uk
www.devonmuseums.net/barnstaple

Curator: Alison Mills

Royal Devon Yeomanry, Royal 1st Devon Yeomanry, North Devon Yeomanry Hussars

The regimental collections of the yeomanry regiments of Devon from 1794 to the present day. Access to the regimental archive is available by appointment. The collection is an outstation of The Keep Military Museum in Dorchester.

Opening Hours: Mon–Fri 9.30am–5pm

Admission: Free. Groups/school parties by arrangement

Facilities: Car parking, toilets, shop, disabled access to ground floor

Blandford Forum

ROYAL SIGNALS MUSEUM

Approximately 4 miles northwest of Blandford Forum on the A350

 Royal Signals Museum, Blandford Camp,
Blandford Forum, Dorset DT11 8RH
T: 01258 482248 F: 01258 482084
E: info@royalsignalsmuseum.com
www.royalsignalsmuseum.com

Director: Colonel CJ Walters
Curator: Stella Ancell

Royal Corps of Signals, Royal Signals, Royal Engineers Signal Service, Royal Engineers Telegraphs

The collection reflects the history of military communications from the Crimea to the present day with displays on the Great War, World War II, Korea, the Falklands and the Gulf War. There is reference to the activities of the Special Operations Executive (SOE), the ATS, Long Range Desert Group and SAS Signals featuring vehicles, motorbikes, uniforms, medals, equipment, memorabilia and trench art. It addresses the history of codes and code-breaking. The museum has a variety of excellent interactive displays with competitions and "fun trails" to appeal to the younger visitor. The Corps library and archive are on-site and may be viewed by appointment. Research facilities are available.

Opening Hours: Weekdays 10am–5pm
Bank holidays and weekends Feb–Oct: 10am–4pm

Admission: Adults £6, seniors £5, children £4, family ticket £17.50. Groups and school parties by arrangement

Facilities: Car and coach parking, restaurant, toilets, lecture room, shop, disabled access, picnic area. No dogs (except guide dogs)

Bodmin

DUKE OF CORNWALL'S LIGHT INFANTRY MUSEUM

Approximately 0.25 miles south of town centre on B3269

 Duke of Cornwall's Light Infantry Regimental Museum
The Keep, Bodmin, Cornwall PL31 1EG
T: 01208 72810 F: 01208 728210
E: dclimus@talk21.com

Curator: Major Trevor Stipling

Somerset and Cornwall Light Infantry, 32nd (Cornwall) Light Infantry, 32nd (or the Cornwall) Regiment of Foot, Colonel Fox's Regiment of Marines, 46th (South Devonshire) Regiment of Foot, 46th (or South Devonshire) Regiment of Foot, 46th Regiment of Foot, Colonel Price's Regiment of Foot

The museum and regimental archive are housed in a listed Militia building built in 1859. From the raising of the regiment in 1702 and the capture of Gibraltar in 1704, the museum covers the history of the County Regiment of Cornwall until its amalgamation in 1959. More recent displays relate to its successor regiments, The Light Infantry and The Rifles. Exhibits include weapons, medals, insignia, uniforms, pictures and George Washington's Bible, captured by the 46th Foot in 1777.

Opening Hours: Mon–Fri 9am–5pm, Sun (Jul and Aug only) 10am–4pm

Admission: Adults/seniors £2, children 50p, groups/school parties by arrangement

Facilities: Car and coach parking, toilets, lecture room, shop, some disabled access. Refreshments adjacent

Bovington

THE TANK MUSEUM [4]

🅿 🧍 🚻 🍴 📷 ♿ 🔲

Bovington Camp is approximately 8 miles from Wareham and two miles from Wool, which is the nearest railway station. There is a bus and taxi service from Wool

The Tank Museum, Bovington Camp,
Dorset BH20 6JG
T: 01929 405096 F: 01929 405360
www.tankmuseum.org

Director: Mr Richard Smith

Royal Armoured Corps, Royal Tank Regiment, Royal Tank Corps, Tank Corps

The Tank Museum houses the most comprehensive collection of armoured vehicles in the world. It tells the story of tanks and armoured warfare illustrated through scientific and technological developments, woven together with stories of human endeavour on the battlefield. An extensive archive and library may be viewed by appointment. See the website for School Holiday and Special Events.

Opening Hours: Daily 10am–5pm. Closed Christmas and New Year's Day

Admission: Adults £10, seniors £9, children £7 (under 5s free). Family Saver tickets also available. All visitors receive an Annual Pass at no extra cost.
School parties and groups: see website or phone for details of special rates

Facilities: Car/coach parking, restaurant, toilets, lecture room, shop, disabled access

Dorchester

THE KEEP MILITARY MUSEUM [5]

🅿 🧍 🚻 📷 ♿ 🎦 ☕

At the western edge of Dorchester, near the Top o' the Town roundabout on the A35

The Keep Military Museum,
Bridport Road,
Dorchester DT1 1RN
T: 01305 264066 F: 01305 250373
E: curator@keepmilitarymuseum.org
www.keepmilitarymuseum.org

Curator: Lieutenant Colonel Charles Cooper

Devonshire and Dorset Regiment, Devonshire Regiment, 11th (or North Devonshire) Regiment of Foot, 11th Regiment of Foot, Duke of Beaufort's Musketeers, Dorset Regiment, 39th (or Dorsetshire) Regiment of Foot, 39th (or East Middlesex) Regiment of Foot, 39th Regiment of Foot, Colonel Richard Coote's Regiment of Foot, 54th (or West Norfolk) Regiment of Foot, 54th Regiment of Foot, 56th Regiment of Foot, Queen's Own Dorset Yeomanry, Dorset Yeomanry, Dorset Militia, Royal Devon Yeomanry, 94 Field Regiment Royal Artillery

The collections of the regiments of Devon and Dorset, including Volunteer and Militia units, from 1685 to the present day. Touch-screen computers, videos and displays tell of the courage, humour and self sacrifice of the soldiers and their families who have served the County Regiments of Devon and Dorset over 300 years.

Opening Hours: Summer (Apr–Sep): Mon–Sat 9.30am–5pm Winter (Oct–Mar): Tue–Sat 9.30am–5pm

Admission: Adults £4, senior/child/student £3, family (2 adults+ up to 3 children) £12. Groups/schools by arrangement; Annual membership: £8

Facilities: Parking, refreshments, toilets, shop, disabled access, picnic area

Gloucester

SOLDIERS OF GLOUCESTERSHIRE MUSEUM [6]

🅿 🧍 🚻 📷 ♿

A 15-minute walk from the city centre, following brown signs to the Historic Docks

Soldiers of Gloucestershire Museum,
Custom House, Gloucester Docks,
Gloucester GL1 2HE
T: 01452 522682 F: 01452 31116
E: enquiries@sogm.co.uk
www.glosters.org.uk

Curator: Major George Streatfield

Royal Gloucestershire, Berkshire and Wiltshire Regiment, Gloucestershire Regiment, 28th (or North Gloucestershire) Regiment of Foot, 28th Regiment of Foot, Colonel Gibson's Regiment of Foot, 61st (or South Gloucestershire) Regiment of Foot, 61st Regiment of Foot, 3rd Foot (2nd Battalion) re-constituted as 61st Foot, Royal Gloucestershire Hussars

The collections of the Regiments of Gloucestershire accumulated over the last 300 years. Exciting and colourful displays include life-sized dioramas, sound effects, archive film and many interesting displays reflecting the history of the County's regiments in the service of the Crown. The library and archive of the Gloucestershire Regiment are housed nearby and may be viewed by appointment.

Q & C
MILITARIA
22 Suffolk Road, Cheltenham GL50 2AQ
Telephone & Fax 01242 519815 Answering Machine
Outside Hours Mobile Telephone 07778 613977
Email qcmilitaria@btconnect.com • Website www.qcmilitaria.com

We wish to Buy for Cash
All items of uniform, helmets and headwear, swords and bayonets,
medals, orders and decorations, badges and uniform furniture,
military memorabilia and trench art.

Top prices Paid
Absolute Discretion Assured
Medals mounted for wearing cased for display and refurbished
miniature medals and mess dress accoutrements supplied

Opening Hours: Jun–Sep: Daily 10am–5pm. Oct–May: Closed on Sundays

Admission: Adults £4.25, seniors/students/concessions £3.25, children £2.25, family ticket (2+2) £13. Groups/schools by appointment

Facilities: Pay and Display parking, toilets, shop, disabled access

Salisbury

ROYAL GLOUCESTERSHIRE, BERKSHIRE AND WILTSHIRE REGIMENT MUSEUM   7

In the Cathedral Close, near the city centre and a 15-minute walk from bus and railway stations

Royal Gloucestershire, Berkshire and Wiltshire Regiment Museum, 58 The Close, Salisbury SP1 2EX
T: 01722 414536 F: 01722 421626
E: curator@thewardrobe.org.uk
www.thewardrobe.org.uk

Curator: Lieutenant Colonel David Chilton

Royal Gloucestershire, Berkshire and Wiltshire Light Infantry, Royal Gloucestershire, Berkshire and Wiltshire Regiment, Duke of Edinburgh's Royal Regiment (Berkshire and Wiltshire), Royal Berkshire Regiment (Princess Charlotte of Wales's), Princess Charlotte of Wales's Berkshire Regiment, 49th Princess of Wales's Herefordshire Regiment of Foot, 49th Herefordshire Regiment of Foot, Colonel Edward Trelawney's Regiment of Foot, 49th (6th or Cotterell's Marines), 66th (Berkshire) Regiment of Foot, 66th Regiment of Foot, Wiltshire Regiment (Duke of Edinburgh's), 62nd (Wiltshire) Regiment of Foot, 62nd Regiment of Foot, 99th (The Duke of Edinburgh's) Regiment of Foot, 99th (Lanarkshire) Regiment of Foot, 99th (Jamaica) Regiment of Foot (disbanded), Volunteers and Militia

Housed on the ground floor of a fine medieval building with a well-stocked riverside garden, this collection covers the history of the County Regiments of Berkshire and Wiltshire and their more recent successors. The regimental library and archive are housed in the same building and may be viewed by appointment. There is an on-site licensed tearoom and restaurant called Bernieres.

Opening Hours: Daily 10am–5pm. Apr–Oct: Open daily Feb, Mar, Nov: Closed Mon; Dec, Jan: Closed

Admission: Adults £2.75, seniors/students/concessions £2, children 75p, family ticket £6. Groups and schools by appointment

Facilities: Shop, restaurant, toilets, disabled access, lecture room, garden

Swindon

ROYAL WILTSHIRE YEOMANRY COLLECTION   8

A (RWY) Squadron Royal Yeomanry, Church Place, Swindon, Wiltshire SN1 5EH
T: 01793 523865 F: 01793 529350
E: arwysqn@tiscali.co.uk
www.yeomanry.co.uk

Curator: Captain A McGinn

A small, private regimental collection covering all aspects of the Royal Wiltshire Yeomanry since its formation in 1794.

Opening Hours: By appointment only

Admission: Free

Facilities: Parking, toilets

Taunton

SOMERSET MILITARY MUSEUM   9

Located in the County Museum in Taunton town centre

Somerset Military Museum, Somerset County Museum, Taunton Castle, Somerset TA1 4AA
T: 01823 320201 F: 01823 320229
E: info@sommilmuseum.org.uk
www.sommilmuseum.org.uk

Curator: Lieutenant Colonel David Eliot

Somerset and Cornwall Light Infantry, Somerset Light Infantry (Prince Albert's), Prince Albert's (Somerset Light Infantry), Prince Albert's (Somersetshire Light Infantry), Prince Albert's Light Infantry (Somersetshire Regiment), 13th or Prince Albert's

Regiment of Light Infantry, The 13th (1st Somersetshire Light Infantry) Regiment, The 13th (1st Somersetshire) Regiment of Foot, 13th Regiment of Foot, Earl of Barrymore's Regiment of Foot (Pearce's Dragoons), The Earl of Huntingdon's Regiment of Foot, Somerset Militia, Somerset Rifle Volunteer Regiments, North Somerset Yeomanry, West Somerset Yeomanry

A comprehensive and well-displayed collection covering the history of the County Regiments of Somerset from 1685, and an explanation of how the former Yeomanry Regiments of Somerset combined with the Somerset Light Infantry Territorials to form an important element of today's County Regiment, The Light Infantry. The coverage of the two World Wars, the Siege of Jellalabad and an extensive medal gallery are of particular note. The Regimental archive of The Somerset Light Infantry and The North Somerset Yeomanry is held at the County Record Office (Tel: 01823 278805) but some archive material is held at the Light Infantry office, 14 Mount Street, Taunton (Tel: 01823 333434).   For details see website. Archive material at the Light Infantry office may be viewed by appointment only.

Opening Hours: Tue–Sat and bank holiday Mondays 10am–5pm; Closed: Good Friday

Admission: Free

Facilities: Shop, toilets, disabled access, adjacent car parking

Warminster

INFANTRY AND SMALL ARMS SCHOOL CORPS WEAPONS COLLECTION

HQ Small Arms School Corps, Land Warfare Centre, Imber Road, Warminster, Wiltshire BA12 0DJ
T: 01985 222487 F: 01985 222211
M: 07952 345901
E: regsecsasc@aol.com

Curator: Major Norman Benson SASC

A comprehensive collection of small arms tracing their development from the 16th century to the present day.

Exhibits include pistols, sub-machine guns, rifles, light and medium machine guns, light and medium mortars and anti-armour weapons. The collection also contains a fine reference library of specialist books and documents covering small arms trials from 1853 to 1939. **The collection is very much for the specialist rather than the casual visitor and is unsuitable for young children.** Visitors are escorted at all times.

Opening Hours: Tue–Thu 9am–4.30pm by appointment only

Admission: Free, but donations are encouraged

Facilities: Parking, toilets and library

The South

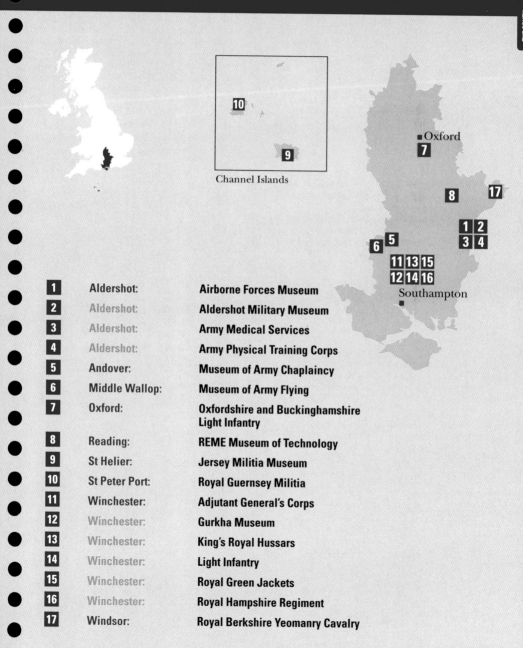

Channel Islands

Oxford

Southampton

1	Aldershot:	**Airborne Forces Museum**
2	Aldershot:	**Aldershot Military Museum**
3	Aldershot:	**Army Medical Services**
4	Aldershot:	**Army Physical Training Corps**
5	Andover:	**Museum of Army Chaplaincy**
6	Middle Wallop:	**Museum of Army Flying**
7	Oxford:	**Oxfordshire and Buckinghamshire Light Infantry**
8	Reading:	**REME Museum of Technology**
9	St Helier:	**Jersey Militia Museum**
10	St Peter Port:	**Royal Guernsey Militia**
11	Winchester:	**Adjutant General's Corps**
12	Winchester:	**Gurkha Museum**
13	Winchester:	**King's Royal Hussars**
14	Winchester:	**Light Infantry**
15	Winchester:	**Royal Green Jackets**
16	Winchester:	**Royal Hampshire Regiment**
17	Windsor:	**Royal Berkshire Yeomanry Cavalry**

Aldershot

AIRBORNE FORCES MUSEUM

Located in Aldershot Military Town. Well signed from Aldershot town and from the A325. Regular buses from Aldershot station

Airborne Forces Museum,
Browning Barracks, Aldershot,
Hampshire GU11 2BU
T: 01252 349619 F: 01252 349203
E: airbornefm@btconnect.com
www.army.mod.uk/para/af_museum

Curator: Mrs Tina Pittock

Parachute Regiment, Glider Pilot Regiment, Special Air Service Regiment, Artist's Rifles

The museum depicts the history of the airborne forces from 1940 to the present day. Using weapons, equipment, dioramas and briefing models it tells the story of the many actions in which members of the Parachute Regiment and other airborne soldiers took part; the early raids, D-Day, Arnhem, Rhine Crossing and more recent campaigns such as the Falklands. Access to the archives is available by appointment.

Opening Hours: Mon–Fri 10am–4.30pm
Weekends and bank holidays 10am–4pm (please phone in advance)

Admission: Adults £3.50, children/seniors £1.50

Facilities: Parking, toilets, shop

Please note the museum is located inside Browning Barracks. Upon arrival at the main gate you will be asked by the Guard to produce some form of photograph identity/driving licence/PRA card. Failure to provide ID can lead to your entry being denied and a wasted journey

ALDERSHOT MILITARY MUSEUM

Regular bus service from town station to Hammersley Road; or turn off A325 to Aldershot Military Town and follow the signs

Aldershot Military Museum,
Queen's Avenue, Aldershot,
Hampshire GU11 2LG
T: 01252 314598 F: 01252 342942
E: musmsa@hants.gov.uk
www.hants.gov.uk/museum/aldershot

Curator: Sally Day

The Aldershot Garrison Collection

The museum tells the story of the home of the British Army and the local history of Aldershot and Farnborough. Photographs, models, displays and an original Victorian barrack room with period uniforms and furniture depict the soldier's daily life, both domestic and military over the last 140 years. The local history gallery shows the growth and development of Aldershot Military Town from 1854 onwards and the birth of British aviation at Farnborough. A selection of richly decorated uniforms from the Flint-Shipman collection is displayed in a military tailor's shop setting. Guns and vehicles are displayed in the Montgomery Gallery.

Opening Hours: Daily 10am–5pm. Closed Christmas and New Year

Admission: Adults £2, seniors/children £1, groups £1.50 or 75p, school parties £1 pp. Family ticket £5

Facilities: Parking, toilets, shop, disabled access, education service

ARMY MEDICAL SERVICES MUSEUM

Taxi from Farnborough or Ash Vale railway stations. By road from M3 exit 4 on A331 for 1.5 miles to exit for Mytchett then follow brown signs for RAMC Museum

Army Medical Services Museum,
Keogh Barracks, Ash Vale,
Aldershot, Hampshire GU12 5RQ
T: 01252 868612 F: 01252 340332
E: museum@keogh72.freeserve.co.uk

Curator: Captain Peter Starling

Royal Army Medical Corps, Army Medical Department Army Hospital Corps, Medical Staff Corps, Royal Army Veterinary Corps, Army Veterinary Corps, Veterinary Medical Department, Royal Army Dental Corps, Army Nursing Service, Territorial Army Nursing Service, Queen Alexandra's Royal Army Nursing Corps, Queen Alexandra's Imperial Military Nursing Service

The museum covers the history of military medicine, veterinary science, nursing and dentistry from 1660 to the present. Included amongst the displays are uniforms, medals, and insignia but also surgical instruments and military ambulances.

Opening Hours: Mon–Fri 10am–3.30pm

Admission: Free

Facilities: Parking, toilets, shop, disabled access

ARMY PHYSICAL TRAINING CORPS MUSEUM 4

By regular bus service from Aldershot, Farnborough and North Camp station, or via M3 using exits 4 and 4a and then A331.

Army Physical Training Corps Museum,
Army School of PT, Fox Lines,
Queen's Avenue, Aldershot,
Hampshire GU11 2LB
T: 01252 347168
E: aspt-regsec@aspt.mod.uk
www.army.mod.uk/aptc

Curator: Major (Ret'd) RJ Kelly

Army Physical Training Corps, Army Physical Training Staff, Army Gymnastics Staff

The items and memorabilia on display tell the story of physical training in the Army from 1860 to the present day. Exhibits concentrate on the theme of the soldier-sportsman and there is an interesting display relating to members of the Corps who have represented their country at International and Olympic level. Access to the Corps archive may be obtained by appointment.

Opening Hours: Mon–Thu 9.30am–4.30pm,
Fri 9.30am–12.30pm; Evenings and weekends by appointment

Admission: Free

Facilities: Parking, toilets, lecture room, shop, disabled access

Andover

MUSEUM OF ARMY CHAPLAINCY 5

Museum of Army Chaplaincy, Armed Forces Chaplaincy Centre, Amport House, Andover, Hampshire SP11 8BG
T: 01264 773144 F: 01264 771042
E: rachdcurator@tiscali.co.uk
www.army.mod.uk/chaps

Curator: David Blake

The collection celebrates the work of army chaplains through the years and includes church silver, uniforms, medals and important archive material.

Opening Hours: Mon–Fri 9am–5pm by appointment only

Admission: Free

Facilities: Parking, toilets, shop, disabled access

Middle Wallop

MUSEUM OF ARMY FLYING 6

Between Salisbury and Andover on the A343

Museum of Army Flying, Middle Wallop,
Stockbridge, Hampshire SO20 8DY
T: 01264 784421 F: 01264 781694
E: enquiries@flying-museum.org.uk
www.flying-museum.org.uk

Director: New appointment pending

Army Aviation, Army Air Corps, Glider Pilot Regiment, Royal Artillery Air Observation Squadrons, Royal Flying Corps

Middle Wallop is the home and training centre for the Army Air Corps. The museum is adjacent to this active airfield and houses a superb collection of aircraft, helicopters and military gliders spanning over 100 years of army aviation. Access to the important archive and research facility is available by appointment.

Opening Hours: Daily 10am–4.30pm (except Christmas week)

Admission: Adults £6, seniors/students £4.50, children (5–16 yrs) £4, family ticket (2+2) £18. Groups by arrangement

Facilities: Parking, restaurant, toilets, lecture room, shop, disabled access, corporate facilities

Oxford

OXFORDSHIRE AND BUCKINGHAMSHIRE LIGHT INFANTRY MUSEUM 7

Off ring road east of city, near Cowley Works. Nearest Bus route 420 Holloway

Oxfordshire and Buckinghamshire Light Infantry Museum, Slade Park TA Barracks, Headington, Oxford OX3 7JJ
T: 01865 780128

Curator: Brigadier Nigel Mogg

Royal Green Jackets, Oxfordshire and Buckinghamshire Light Infantry, 43rd (Monmouthshire Light Infantry) Regiment of Foot, 43rd (or the Monmouthshire) Regiment of Foot (Light Infantry), 43rd (or The Monmouthshire) Regiment of Foot, Colonel Fowke's Regiment of Foot, 54th Foot (re-numbered 43rd Foot), 52nd (Oxfordshire Light Infantry) Regiment, 52nd (Oxfordshire) Regiment of Foot, 52nd Regiment of Foot, 54th Regiment of Foot

A small but comprehensive collection of uniforms, weapons and other artefacts covering the history of the Regiment from its formation in 1741 to its amalgamation into the Royal Green Jackets in 1966.

Opening Hours: Daily 10am–4pm by appointment only

Admission: Free

Facilities: Parking, toilets, disabled access

Reading
REME MUSEUM OF TECHNOLOGY   8

By train to Reading/Wokingham, then by bus. By road, along A327 from Reading to Arborfield Garrison

REME Museum of Technology,
Isaac Newton Road, Arborfield, Reading,
Berkshire RG2 9NJ
T: 0118 9763375 F: 0118 9762017
E: enquiries@rememuseum.org.uk
www.rememuseum.org.uk

Director: Lieutenant Colonel IW Cleasby MBE

Reflecting the history of the Corps of REME and its soldiers, the museum has a 1950s Guardroom display and a main museum display with medals, dioramas, equipment and trades. A vehicle exhibition hall houses 20 specialist vehicles and a helicopter. A weapons display is currently under construction. A calendar of Family Events is published and a comprehensive Education Service is available to schools. Please see website for details. Teachers' Packs are available on request.

Opening Hours: Mon–Thu 9am–4.30pm, Fri 9am–4pm, Sun 11am–4pm

Admission: Adults £3.50, seniors £3, groups £3 for 10+, children £2.50 (under 5s free), family ticket £10, school parties by arrangement

Facilities: Parking, restaurant, toilets, lecture room, shop, disabled access, corporate facilities

St Helier, Jersey
JERSEY MILITIA MUSEUM   9

Jersey Militia Museum Collection,
Elizabeth Castle, St Aubin's Bay,
St Helier, Jersey JE2 3NF
T: 01534 633300 F: 01534 633301
E: museum@jerseyheritagetrust.org
www.jerseyheritagetrust.org

Director: Jonathan Carter

A small collection of objects associated with the Jersey Militia and the military history of the island.

Opening Hours: Daily 10am–6pm. Last admission 5pm

Admission: Adults £5.40, seniors and students £4.50, children under 6 free. Family £15.40, groups and school parties by appointment

Facilities: Toilets, shop, refreshments

St Peter Port, Guernsey
ROYAL GUERNSEY MILITIA   10

Royal Guernsey Militia Collection,
Castle Cornet, St Peter Port,
Guernsey GY1 1AU
T: 01481 721657 F: 01481 714021
E: m.harvey@museums.gov.gg
www.museums.gov.gg

Curator/Social History Officer:
Matt Harvey

Telling the story of the Royal Guernsey Militia (later the Royal Guernsey Light Infantry) this museum houses many regimental relics. It is currently closed, ahead of a refurbishment which seeks to incorporate many items from the unique Spencer Collection of Channel Islands military uniforms, buttons and badges. Anyone wishing to view Militia items from the collection during the museum's closure, for the purposes of research or to view items relating to their family, should contact the Social History Officer to arrange access.

Winchester

ADJUTANT GENERAL'S CORPS MUSEUM   11

At the upper end of the city centre, close to the Great Hall and Westgate

Adjutant General's Corps Museum Collection,
The Guardroom, Peninsula Barracks,
Romsey Road, Winchester,
Hampshire SO23 8TS
T: 01962 877826
E: agcmuseum@milnet.uk.net

Curator: Mr Ian Bailey

Adjutant General's Corps, Corps of Royal Military Police and Provost Staff Corps, Royal Army Pay Corps, Army Pay Corps, Army Pay Department, Royal Army Education Corps, Army Education Corps, Corps of Army Schoolmasters, Women's Royal Army Corps, Auxiliary Training Service, Women's Army Auxiliary Corps, Army Legal Corps, Army Legal Staff

The Adjutant General's Corps was formed in 1992 and the museum tells the histories of those corps from which it was formed using text, images, objects, uniforms and realistic figure reconstructions. The museum was opened in November 2003 by HM The Queen, Colonel Commandant of the AGC.

Opening Hours: Tue–Sat 10am–5pm,
Sun (Easter–September) 12pm–4pm

Admission: Free

Facilities: Parking (by arrangement), toilets, café

THE GURKHA MUSEUM   12

At the upper end of the city centre, close to the Great Hall and Westgate

Gurkha Museum, Peninsula Barracks, Romsey Road, Winchester, Hampshire SO23 8TS
T: 01962 842832/843659
F: 01962 877597
E: curator@thegurkhamuseum.co.uk
www.thegurkhamuseum.co.uk

Curator: Major Gerald Davies

Royal Gurkha Rifles, 1st King George V's Own Gurkha Rifles (The Malaun Regiment), 2nd King Edward VII's Own Gurkha Rifles (The Sirmoor Rifles), 3rd Queen Alexandra's Own Gurkha Rifles, 4th Prince of Wales's Own Gurkha Rifles, 5th Royal Gurkha Rifles (Frontier Force), 6th Queen Elizabeth's Own Gurkha Rifles, 7th Duke Of Edinburgh's Own Gurkha Rifles, 8th Gurkha Rifles, 9th Gurkha Rifles, 10th Princess Mary's Own Gurkha Rifles, 11th Gurkha Rifles (1918-1922), Queen's Gurkha Engineers, Queen's Gurkha Signals, Queen's Own Gurkha Transport Regiment, Western or Bettiah Corps (1813-1826), Eastern or Rungpore Battalion (1815-1830), 2nd Nusseri Battalion (1815-1816), Gorakhpore Hill Rangers (1815-1816), Sylhet Frontier Corps (1817-1823), 4th Regiment of Infantry, Shah Shooja's Force (1840-1843), 2nd Assam Sebundy Corps (1839-1844), Nusseree Battalion (1850-1861), 7th Gurkha Rifles (1902-1907), 153 (Gurkha) Parachute Battalion (1941-1947), 154 (Gurkha) Parachute Battalion (1943-1946), 5th/3rd Gurkha Rifles (1942), 25th Gurkha Rifles (1942-1946), 26th Gurkha Rifles (1943-1946), 14th Gurkha Rifles (1943-1946), 29th Gurkha Rifles (1943-1946), 38th Gurkha Rifles (1943-1946), 56th Gurkha Rifles (1943-1946), 710th Gurkha Rifles (1943- 1946), Boys Company (1948-1968), Gurkha Military Police (1949-1970), Staff Band Brigade of Gurkhas, Gurkha Independent Parachute Company (1961-1971), Assam Rifles, Burma Military Police (1886-1948), Burma Frontier Force (1886-1948), Burma Regiment (1886-1948), Burma Rifles (1915-1942), Jammu and Kashmir Units, 11th Gorkha Rifles

The Gurkha Museum, tells the story of Gurkha service to the Crown since 1815, covering the Indian Mutiny, North-West Frontier, both world wars, post-Empire conflicts in Vietnam, Indonesia, Hong Kong, and the Falkland Islands and a variety of more recent UN operations including Zaire, the Gulf, Bosnia, Kosovo, East Timor, Sierra Leone, Iraq and Afghanistan. The collection also reflects the art and culture of Nepal. There is also an extensive library and archive facility available by prior appointment.

Opening Hours: Mon–Sat 10am–5pm (last entry 4.30pm), Sun 12pm–4pm (last entry 3.30pm)

Admission: Adults £2, seniors £1, children and servicemen free. Groups and school parties by arrangement

Facilities: Parking, toilets, lecture room, shop, disabled access, corporate events

"HORSEPOWER" – THE MUSEUM OF THE KING'S ROYAL HUSSARS   13

At the upper end of the city centre, close to the Great Hall and Westgate

The King's Royal Hussars Museum,
Peninsula Barracks, Romsey Road,
Winchester, Hampshire SO23 8TS
T: 01962 828541 F: 01962 828538
E: beresford@krhmuseum.freeserve.co.uk
www.krh.org/museum.htm

Curator: Major Patrick Beresford

The King's Royal Hussars, The Royal Hussars (Prince of Wales's Own), 10th Royal Hussars (Prince of Wales's Own), 10th (Prince of Wales's Own Royal) Hussars, 10th (Prince of Wales's Own)

Hussars, 10th (Prince of Wales's Own) Light Dragoons, 10th Dragoons, 11th Hussars (Prince Albert's Own), 11th (Prince Albert's Own) Hussars, 11th Light Dragoons, 11th Dragoons, Gore's Dragoons, Churchill's Dragoons, Cobham's Dragoons, Honeywood's Dragoons, Kerr's Dragoons

A comprehensive collection of uniforms, medals, weapons, paintings, photographs, regimental silver and guidons trace the history of The King's Royal Hussars and its predecessor regiments from their foundation in 1715 to the present day. The museum has recently re-opened after extensive refurbishment. Access to the archives is available by prior appointment.

Opening Hours: Tue–Fri 10am–12.45pm and 1.15pm–4pm. Sat, Sun and holidays 12pm–4pm

Admission: Free

Facilities: Parking, toilets, shop, disabled access

LIGHT INFANTRY MUSEUM

At the upper end of the city centre, close to the Great Hall and Westgate

Light Infantry Museum, Peninsula Barracks, Romsey Road, Winchester, Hampshire SO23 8TS
T: 01962 828550 F: 01962 828534
www.lightinfantry.co.uk

Curator: Major John Spiers

With several museums elsewhere dedicated to the former County Light Infantry regiments, this museum tells the story of The Light Infantry from its inception in 1968. Displays cover the Regiment's operations in Northern Ireland, the Gulf War and in support of the United Nations in a variety of theatres. The regimental archive may be viewed by appointment.

Opening Hours: Tue–Sat and bank holidays 10am–4pm (closed for lunch). Sun 12pm–4pm

Admission: Free

Facilities: Parking nearby, shop, toilets, disabled access

ROYAL GREEN JACKETS MUSEUM

At the upper end of the city centre, close to the Great Hall and Westgate

Royal Green Jackets Museum, Peninsula Barracks, Romsey Road, Winchester, Hampshire SO23 8TS
T: 01962 828549 F: 01962 828500
E: museum@royalgreenjackets.co.uk
www.royalgreenjackets.co.uk

Curator: Major Ken Gray

The Rifles, Royal Green Jackets, 1st Green Jackets, Oxfordshire and Buckinghamshire Light Infantry, 43rd (Monmouthshire Light Infantry) Regiment of Foot, 43rd (or the Monmouthshire) Regiment of Foot (Light Infantry), 43rd (or the Monmouthshire) Regiment of Foot, 43rd Regiment of Foot, Colonel Fowke's Regiment of Foot, 54th Foot (re-numbered 43rd Foot), 52nd (Oxfordshire Light Infantry) Regiment, 52nd (Oxfordshire) Regiment of Foot, Colonel Lambton's Regiment of Foot, 54th Foot (re-numbered 52nd Foot), 2nd Green Jackets (King's Royal Rifle Corps), King's Royal Rifle Corps, 60th or The King's Royal Rifle Corps Regiment of Foot, 60th or The Duke of York's Own Rifle Corps, 60th (Royal American) Regiment of Foot, 62nd or The Royal American Regiment of Foot (re-numbered 60th Foot), 3rd Green Jackets (Rifle Brigade), Rifle Brigade (Prince Consort's Own), Rifle Brigade (The Prince Consort's Own), Prince Consort's Own Rifle Brigade, Rifle Brigade, 95th Rifle Regiment, 1800 Experimental Corps of Riflemen or Rifle Corps

An outstanding collection of uniforms, weapons, silver, paintings and medals, including 34 of the Regiment's 59 Victoria Crosses, all impressively displayed, record the history of the Royal Green Jackets and its antecedent regiments from 1741 to the present day. Amongst several models is a magnificent diorama of Waterloo with 22,000 model soldiers and horses and an accompanying sound and light commentary. The regimental archive is housed in a separate building on site and may be viewed by appointment.

Opening Hours: Mon–Sat 10am–5pm, Sun 12pm–4pm. Closed mid-Nov to 1 Mar

Admission: Adult £2, seniors/students/children £1, family £6

Facilities: Parking nearby, toilets, shop, disabled access

ROYAL HAMPSHIRE REGIMENT MUSEUM   16

Just off the city centre, near the Great Hall and other regimental museums

 Royal Hampshire Regiment Museum,
Serle's House, Southgate Street,
Winchester, Hampshire SO23 9EG
T: 01962 863658 F: 01962 863658
E: serleshouse@aol.com
www.royalhampshireregimentmuseum.co.uk

Curator: Michael Stephens

Princess of Wales's Royal Regiment (Queen's and Royal Hampshires), Royal Hampshire Regiment, Hampshire Regiment, 37th (or the North Hampshire) Regiment of Foot, 37th Regiment of Foot, Gray's Regiment of Foot, Stuart's Regiment of Foot, de Jean's Regiment of Foot, Munro's Regiment of Foot, Ponsonby's Regiment of Foot, Murray's Regiment of Foot, Hinchinbroke's Regiment of Foot, Fane's Regiment of Foot, Windress's Regiment of Foot, Meredith's Regiment of Foot, 67th (or South Hampshire) Regiment of Foot, 67th Regiment of Foot, 2nd Battalion 20th Foot, 67th (South Hampshire) Regiment of Foot, 6th (Duke of Connaught's Own) Battalion The Hampshire Regiment, 8th (Princess Beatrice's Own Isle of Wight Rifles) Battalion The Hampshire Regiment, 11th (Royal Militia of Jersey) Battalion The Hampshire Regiment.

The collection of Hampshire's County Regiment, the Militia, Rifle Volunteers and Volunteers from 1702 onwards. The regimental archive is held in the same building and may be viewed by appointment.

Opening Hours: Mon–Fri 10am–4pm
Apr–Oct: weekends and bank holidays 12pm–4pm

Admission: Free, but donations most welcome

Facilities: Toilets, shop, memorial garden with seating

ROYAL BERKSHIRE YEOMANRY CAVALRY MUSEUM   17

At the junction of Wood Street and Bolton Street. From town centre follow signs to the Great Park and turn right into Bolton Street at the 40mph sign

 Royal Berkshire Yeomanry Cavalry Museum, TA Centre, Bolton Road,
Windsor, Berkshire SL4 3JG
T: 01753 860600 F: 01753 854946
E: 32sigregt-94sqnpsao@tanet.mod.uk
www.army.mod.uk/royalsignals/94sigsqn.htm

Curator: Brigadier AP Verey and Captain AG French

The museum contains a well-displayed and comprehensive collection tracing the history of the Regiment since its beginnings in 1794.

Opening Hours: Tue 7.30pm–9.30pm by appointment only

Admission: Free

Facilities: Parking nearby, toilets, limited disabled access

South East

LONDON

1 2
10
9
11
3
8
5

Southampton
4
Brighton
12 6 7

1	Camberley:	**Royal Logistic Corps**
2	Camberley:	**Royal Military Academy Sandhurst**
3	Canterbury:	**Buffs, Royal East Kent Regiment**
4	Chichester:	**Royal Military Police Museum**
5	Dover:	**Princess of Wales's Royal Regiment and Queen's Regiment**
6	Eastbourne:	**Queen's Royal Irish Hussars**
7	Eastbourne:	**Royal Sussex Regiment**
8	Edenbridge:	**Kent and Sharpshooters Yeomanry**
9	Gillingham:	**Royal Engineers**
10	Guildford:	**Queen's Royal Surrey Regiment**
11	Maidstone:	**Queen's Own Royal West Kent Regiment**
12	Newhaven:	**Sussex and Surrey Yeomanry**

Camberley

ROYAL LOGISTIC CORPS MUSEUM

Train to Brookwood, then bus 455, 454 or by car via M3 (Junct 3) and along B3015

Royal Logistic Corps Museum,
Princess Royal Barracks, Deepcut,
Camberley, Surrey GU16 6RW
T: 01252 833371 F: 01252 833484
E: information@rlcmuseum.com
www.army-rlc.uk

Director: Sue Lines

Royal Logistic Corps, Royal Corps of Transport, Royal Army Service Corps, Army Service Corps, Commissariat and Transport Corps, Commissariat and Transport Department, Control Department, Commissariat Department, Military Train, Land Transport Corps, Royal Waggon Train, Corps of Waggoners, Royal Army Ordnance Corps, Army Ordnance Corps, Army Ordnance Department, Ordnance Store Corps, Ordnance Store Department, Ordnance Store Branch, Control Department, Military Store Staff Corps, Military Stores Department, Corps of Armourer-Sergeants, Royal Pioneer Corps, Pioneer Corps, Auxiliary Military Pioneer Corps, Labour Corps, Army Catering Corps, Royal Engineers Postal and Courier Service

The museum, recently modernised and refurbished, houses a comprehensive collection relating to the history and activities of the Royal Logistic Corps and its several antecedent corps. Displays include uniforms, medals, weapons and historical artefacts portraying the development of military logistics from the Middle Ages to the present day. Access to the extensive Corps archive is available by appointment.

Opening Hours: Tue–Fri 10am–4pm, Sat (Easter–Sep) 12pm–4pm. Closed Sun, Mon, public holidays and between Christmas and New Year

Admission: Free. Groups and school parties by appointment

Facilities: Parking, toilets, shop, disabled access

ROYAL MILITARY ACADEMY SANDHURST

Train to Camberley or London-Fareham coach to Cambridge Hotel. Main entrance on A30

Royal Military Academy Sandhurst Collection, Camberley, Surrey GU15 4PQ
T: 01276 412489/2483 F: 01276 412595
Research enquiries to:
dr.morton@rmas.mod.uk

Curator: Dr Peter Thwaites
Archivist: Dr Anthony Morton

Royal Military Academy Sandhurst, Royal Military Academy Woolwich, Royal Military College Sandhurst

The small collection includes displays of uniforms, paintings, photographs and other artefacts relating to the history of the Royal Military Academy Sandhurst and its predecessors. The Academy's historic archive, including the gentlemen cadet registers, forms part of the collection.

Opening Hours: By appointment only

Facilities: Parking, toilets

Canterbury

THE BUFFS, ROYAL EAST KENT REGIMENT MUSEUM COLLECTION

Situated in the city centre on the first floor of the Beaney Institute

The Buffs, Royal East Kent Regiment Museum Collection, Royal Museum and Art Gallery, 18 High Street, Canterbury, Kent CT1 2RA
T: 01227 452747 F: 01227 455047
E: martin.crowther@canterbury.gov.uk

Educational Development Manager:
Martin Crowther

Princess of Wales's Royal Regiment (Queen's and Royal Hampshires), Queen's Own Buffs, Royal Kent Regiment, Buffs (Royal East Kent Regiment), Buffs (East Kent Regiment), 3rd (East Kent, The Buffs) Regiment, 3rd (or the East Kent) Regiment of Foot, 3rd (or The Buffs) Regiment of Foot, Prince George of Denmark's Regiment of Foot

A collection reflecting the history of one of England's oldest infantry regiments. The impressive displays of pictures, medals, uniforms, mess silver and other artefacts trace the world-wide history of the Regiment from is formation in Elizabethan days to its amalgamation in 1961. They include small sections on the East Kent Volunteers and Militia. The Buffs Collection is now owned by the National Army Museum. All research enquiries should be addressed to Dr Alastair Massie, Head of Archives, Photographs, Film and Sound, National Army Museum, Royal Hospital Road, Chelsea, London SW3 4HT: Tel 020 7730 0717, e-mail amassie@national-army-museum.ac.uk

Opening Hours: Mon–Sat 10am–5pm

Admission: Free. Groups and schools parties by appointment

Facilities: Toilets, shop

All information is correct at the time of going to press, but **you are advised to contact museums before making a visit**

23

Chichester

ROYAL MILITARY POLICE MUSEUM

From railway station by 260 bus to museum on A286 Chichester-Midhurst road

Royal Military Police Museum.
Roussillon Barracks, Broyle Road,
Chichester, West Sussex PO19 4BN
T: 01243 534225 F: 01234 534288
E:museum@rhqrmp.freeserve.co.uk.
www.army.mod.uk/rhqrmp

Curator: Miss Rhona Mitchell

Corps of Royal Military Police, Corps of Military Police, Military Foot Police, Military Mounted Police, Military Provost Staff Corps, Military Prison Staff Corps

The museum traces the history of military police from Tudor times to the present day. Recent operations, including those in support of the United Nations and NATO, are amongst the displays. A library and limited research facilities are available by arrangement with the curator.

N.B. In the near future the museum is moving to The Defence Police College, Southwick Park, Fareham, Hampshire, PO17 6EJ. All visits are therefore by arrangement with the curator. For news of the move and details of re-opening, see the museum website.

Dover

PRINCESS OF WALES'S ROYAL REGIMENT AND QUEEN'S REGIMENT MUSEUM

Access by car, minibus or taxi from town centre

Princess of Wales's Royal Regiment and Queen's Regiment Museum, 5 Keep Yard, Dover Castle, Dover, Kent CT16 1HU
T: 01304 240121 F: 01304 240121
E: pwrrqueensmuseum@tinyworld.co.uk
www.army.mod.uk/pwrr

Curator: RHQ, PWRR, Howe Barracks, Canterbury CT1 1JY
T: 01227 818053 F: 01227 818057
E: rhq@123pwrr.co.uk

Princess of Wales's Royal Regiment (Queen's and Royal Hampshires), Queen's Regiment, 1st Bn Queen's Regiment (Queen's Surrey), 2nd Bn Queen's Regiment (Queen's Own Buffs), 3rd Bn Queen's Regiment (Royal Sussex), 4th Bn Queen's Regiment (Middlesex)

The collection traces the history of the Princess of Wales's Royal Regiment – direct successor of twelve forebear regiments – through four-and-a-quarter centuries of service to the Crown. It

begins in 1572 with the deployment of a Tudor company to support the Dutch in their war against the Spanish, moving on to the raising of a regiment in 1661 to garrison the North African port of Tangier, which earned the first ever awarded battle honour "Tangier 1662-80". A series of displays, interactive videos and recordings takes the visitor right up to the Regiment's most recent operations in support of the UN and NATO.

Opening Hours: Apr–Sep: 10am–6pm. Oct: 10am–5pm. Nov–Mar: 10am–4pm

Admission: Free with Castle entry. Groups and school parties by appointment

Facilities: Parking, refreshments, toilets, lecture room, shop

Eastbourne

QUEEN'S ROYAL IRISH HUSSARS MUSEUM

On the seafront 0.5 miles east of the pier. A 20-minute walk from the station or Nos 1, 2, 3, 9, 22 buses from the town centre stop nearby on Seaside Road

Queen's Royal Irish Hussars Museum,
Part of the Queen's Royal Hussars Collection, Redoubt Fortress, Eastbourne, East Sussex BN22 7AQ
T: 01323 410300 F: 01323 439882
E: redoubtmuseum@eastbourne.gov.uk
www.eastbournemuseums.co.uk

Curator: Major Patrick Timmons
London Office: 020 7756 2274

Queen's Royal Irish Hussars, 8th King's Royal Irish Hussars, 8th Light Dragoons, Cunningham's Dragoons, 4th Queen's Own Hussars, 4th Light Dragoons

An important collection covering this distinguished Regiment's history from its formation in 1693 to the Gulf War. Displays include items from the Charge of the Light Brigade and a fine collection of medals. The Redoubt, built in 1804-10, is a massive defensive work originally housing 250 troops. The fortress has been restored, and provides an interesting and fitting location for its military museums.

Opening Hours: Apr–Nov: Tue–Sun 10am–5pm. Closed Mondays except bank holidays

Admission: Adults £3.50, seniors/children/groups 10+/school parties £3. Further concessions available

Facilities: Café, toilets, shop

ROYAL SUSSEX REGIMENT MUSEUM **7**

On the seafront 0.5 miles east of the pier. A 20-minute walk from the station or Nos 1, 2, 3, 9, 22 buses from the town centre stop nearby on Seaside Road

Royal Sussex Regimental Collection, Redoubt, Royal Parade Eastbourne, East Sussex BN22 7AQ
T: 01323 410300 F: 01323 438827
E: redoubtmuseum@eastbourne.gov.uk

www.eastbourne.gov.uk/leisure/museums-galleries/redoubt
www.eastbournemuseums.co.uk

Curator: Fran Stovold

Royal Sussex Regiment, 35th (Royal Sussex) Regiment, 35th (or The Sussex) Regiment of Foot, 35th (or The Dorsetshire) Regiment of Foot, 35th Regiment of Foot, Earl of Donegal's Regiment of Foot – The Belfast Regiment, 107th Bengal Infantry Regiment, 3rd (Bengal Light Infantry) Regiment, 3rd (Bengal European Light Infantry) Regiment (Honourable East India Company)

The collection of the County Regiment of Sussex covering its history from the raising of its antecedent regiments in 1701 under the 3rd Earl of Donegall, to its amalgamation into The Queen's Regiment in 1966. Collection highlights include a display of rare headdress badges, and impressive collections of uniforms and medals, as well as a German staff car captured in the desert in 1943.

The collection is displayed within the Redoubt Fortress. This circular Napoleonic fort is one of the best preserved in the country. Built between 1804-10 at a time when Napoleon was threatening to invade England it forms, along with 74 Martello towers, a string of coastal defences stretching from Folkestone to Seaford. Originally housing anything up to 250 soldiers the Redoubt provides the perfect setting for this regimental collection. Alongside the collections of The Queen's Royal Irish Hussars and the Sussex Combined Services it forms the largest military museum in the south.

Opening Hours: 15 Apr–12 Nov: Tue–Sun 10am–5.00pm. Closed Mon except bank holidays. Otherwise by appointment

Admission: Adults £4, seniors £3, children £2, groups 10+ £3.20, school parties £1.50, family ticket £8 (2 adults + 2 children) £6 (1 + 3 children). Eastbourne residents half price with Leisure Card

Facilities: Toilets, shop

Edenbridge

KENT AND SHARPSHOOTERS YEOMANRY MUSEUM **8**

Off B2026 between Sevenoaks and East Grinstead in the village of Hever. Taxi from Edenbridge town, 3 miles away

Kent and Sharpshooters Yeomanry Museum, Hever Castle, Edenbridge, Kent TN8 7NG
T: 01732 865224
E: ksymuseum@aol.com
www.ksymuseum.org.uk

Curator: Major Boris Mollo

Royal East Kent Mounted Rifles, Queen's Own West Kent Yeomanry, The Kent Yeomanry, 3rd County of London Yeomanry (Sharpshooters), 23rd London Armoured Company (Sharpshooters), 4th County of London Yeomanry (Sharpshooters), 3rd/4th County of London Yeomanry (Sharpshooters), Kent and County of London Yeomanry (Sharpshooters), Kent and Sharpshooters Yeomanry

Uniforms, medals, badges, pictures and photographs reflecting the history of the Regiment and its predecessors. A further display and the regimental archive may be seen by appointment at Sharpshooters House, Mitcham Road, Croydon, Surrey CR0 3RU. Tel: 020 8688 2138.

Opening Hours: 1 Mar–30 Nov: 12pm–6pm daily. Last admissions at 5pm

Admission: Adults £9.80, seniors £8.20, children £5.30, family (2+2) £24.90. Groups by appointment

Note: When Hever Castle is very busy the Regimental Museum may be closed. Visitors are advised to telephone ahead to confirm arrangements.

Facilities: Parking, refreshments, toilets, shop, disabled access

All information is correct at the time of going to press, but **you are advised to contact museums before making a visit**

25

Gillingham

ROYAL ENGINEERS MUSEUM 🟨9

Taxi or 1-mile walk from Gillingham station. By road from Gillingham: A231 from town centre towards Chatham, turn right at traffic lights into Prince Arthur Road. From Chatham: A231 from town centre towards Gillingham, left at roundabout into Wood Street and left at traffic lights into Prince Arthur Road

Royal Engineers Museum,
Brompton Barracks, Prince Arthur Road,
Gillingham, Kent ME4 4UG
T: 01634 822839 F: 01634 822371
E: mail@re-museum.co.uk
www.remuseum.org.uk

Curator: Rebecca Cheney

Corps of Royal Engineers, Royal Engineers, Corps of Royal Sappers and Miners, Corps of Royal Military Artificers, Indian Engineers including Bengal, Bombay and Madras groups, East India Company Engineer Groups, Royal Engineers Submarine Service, Royal Engineers Bomb Disposal, Military Survey

The Royal Engineers Museum and Library tell the story of the Corps of Royal Engineers and military engineering. It is a story about the Sappers and their courage, creativity and innovation. In peace and war the Corps has been everywhere and involved in everything. The museum galleries display exquisite Chinese embroideries given to General Gordon, drawings, letters and airgraphs, paintings and fine uniforms alongside Zulu shields from Rorke's Drift, tanks, torpedoes, bridges and chemical weapons. The Library, founded in 1813, holds material as diverse as 1860s photographs of Canada, classic military histories and World War I unit war diaries.

Opening Hours: Tue–Fri 9am–5pm, Sat/Sun/bank holidays 11.30am–5pm; Closed Mon, Christmas week and New Year's Day

Admission: Adults £5.75, seniors/students/children (5-16) £3, family (2+2 or 1+3) £14.50. Annual tickets: adults £13.80, seniors/students/children £7.20, family £34.50

Facilities: Parking, toilets, lecture room, shop, disabled access

Guildford

QUEEN'S ROYAL SURREY REGIMENT MUSEUM 🟨10

The museum stands 300 yards north of the A246 and A247 junction. From Clandon station, Guildford-Leatherhead bus to Clandon crossroads

Queen's Royal Surrey Regiment Museum,
Clandon Park, Guildford, Surrey GU4 7RQ
T: 01483 223419 F: 01483 223419
E: qrsregimentalmuseum@btconnect.com
www.queensroyalsurreys.org.uk

Curator: Ian Chatfield

Princess of Wales's Royal Regiment (Queen's and Royal Hampshires), Queen's Royal Surrey Regiment, Queen's Royal Regiment (West Surrey), Queen's (Royal West Surrey) Regiment, Royal West Surrey Regiment (The Queen's), Royal West Surreys, Princess of Wales's Own Regiment of Foot, Queen's Royal Regiment, Queen's (Second) Royal Regiment of Foot, Queen's Own Royal Regiment of Foot, Queen Dowager's Regiment of Foot, Queen Dowager's Regiment, Queen's Regiment, Henry Mordaunt, Earl of Peterborough – The Tangier Regiment, East Surrey Regiment, 31st (Huntingdonshire) Regiment, 31st (or Huntingdonshire) Regiment of Foot, 31st Regiment of Foot, Villier's Regiment of Marines, Goring's Marines, Churchill's Marines, Luttrell's Marines, 70th (Surrey) Regiment, 70th (or The Glasgow Lowland) Regiment of Foot, Glasgow Greys, 70th (or The Surrey) Regiment of Foot, 70th Regiment of Foot

Housed in the National Trust property of Clandon Park, the museum tells the story of England's senior infantry regiment and its antecedent three County Regiments of Surrey in a comprehensive display of important objects covering the period 1661 to the present day. Researchers are welcome but are advised to contact the curator for an appointment.

Opening Hours: Mar–end Oct: Tue, Wed, Thu, Sun and bank holidays 12pm–5pm

Admission: Free, donations welcome

Facilities: Parking, refreshments, toilets, shop, disabled access

For a detailed map, go to **www.streetmap.co.uk** and type in the post code of the museum

WALLIS & WALLIS   EST. 1928

WEST STREET AUCTION GALLERIES, LEWES, SUSSEX, ENGLAND BN7 2NJ
TEL: +44 (0)1273 480208 FAX: +44 (0)1273 476562

BRITAIN'S SPECIALIST AUCTIONEERS OF MILITARIA, ARMS, ARMOUR & MEDALS

ELEVEN AUCTIONS OF ANTIQUE ARMS, ARMOUR, MILITARIA AND MEDALS HELD ANNUALLY

Colour illustrated catalogues £9.50

Connoisseur Auction catalogues
(Spring & Autumn) £14.00

Ten previous regular auction
catalogues, complete with prices
realised, available price £23.00

(Postage included)

*Officer's sabretache of the 10th (The Prince of
Wales's Own Royal) Hussars. Realised £1,650
in a recent Connoisseur Collectors' auction.*

NO VENDORS COMMISSION CHARGED TO REGISTERED CHARITIES

Auction dates and Entry Forms available on request

No charge of payment by credit card

VISA

email: auctions@wallisandwallis.co.uk   web site: http://www.wallisandwallis.co.uk

Maidstone

QUEEN'S OWN ROYAL WEST KENT REGIMENT COLLECTION

By road from London leave M20 at J6, from Folkestone leave M20 at J8 then join A20. Trains to Maidstone East station

Queen's Own Royal West Kent Regiment Museum Collection, Maidstone Museum and Art Gallery, St Faith's Street, Maidstone, Kent ME4 1LH
T: 01622 602838
E: qorwkmuseum@maidstone.gov.uk

Curator: The Manager, Maidstone Museum Service

Queen's Own Royal West Kent Regiment, Royal West Kent Regiment (Queen's Own), Queen's Own (Royal West Kent Regiment), 50th (Queen's Own) Regiment, 50th or The Queen's Regiment of Foot, 50th (or the Duke of Clarence's) Regiment of Foot, 50th (or West Kent) Regiment of Foot, 50th Regiment of Foot, 52nd Regiment of Foot, 97th (Earl of Ulster's) Regiment of Foot, 97th Regiment of Foot, 20th London Regiment, Deptford Volunteers, Loyal Greenwich Water Fencibles, Loyal Greenwich Volunteer Infantry, 3rd Kent Rifle Volunteers. 2nd Volunteer Bn The Queen's Own (Royal West Kent Regiment), 20th (County of London) Bn The London Regiment, 20th London Regiment (The Queen's Own), 34th (The Queen's Own, Royal West Kent) Anti Aircraft Battalion Royal Engineers, 34th (The Queen's Own, Royal West Kent) Searchlight Regiment Royal Artillery TA, 569 Searchlight Regiment RA (QORWK) TA, 569 (The Queen's Own)(M) LAA/SL Regiment RA TA, Q (The Queen's Own) Battery 265 LAA Regiment RA TA, 6th (Cyclist) Battalion The Queen's Own Royal West Kent Regiment, Kent Cyclists Battalion

A comprehensive regimental collection of uniforms, weapons, medals, pictures and campaign relics. It includes the personal effects of a number of distinguished soldiers such as Field Marshal Viscount Hardinge and General Sir Charles Napier.

Opening Hours: Mon–Fri 10am–5.15pm, Sun 11am–4pm

Admission: Free

Facilities: Refreshments, toilets, shop, disabled access

Newhaven

SUSSEX AND SURREY YEOMANRY COLLECTION

On A259 coast road. 1 mile from town centre

Sussex and Surrey Yeomanry Museum Collection, Newhaven Fort, Newhaven, East Sussex BN9 9DL
T: 01273 517622
E: info@newhavenfort.org.uk
www.newhavenfort.org.uk

Curator: Keith Fuller
T: 01273 611055 E: founded1794@aol.com

Opening Hours: 1 Mar–31 Oct: 10.30am–6pm daily (5pm in Oct)

Admission: Adults £5.50, seniors/students £4.50, children £3.60, family (2+2/3) £16.50. Groups and school parties by appointment

Facilities: Coach parking (by appt), café, toilets. Phone in advance to arrange disabled drop-off point and access

London

■ Watford   ■ Enfield

4 11
2 3 5
12 9 7
6
1 ■ Woolwich

10 Kingston upon-Thames

■ Croydon

8

1	Firepower! Royal Artillery Museum
2	Guards Museum
3	Household Cavalry
4	Honourable Artillery Company
5	Inns of Court and City Yeomanry
6	London Irish Rifles
7	London Scottish Regiment
8	Princess Louise's Kensington Regiment
9	Royal Hospital Chelsea
10	Royal Military School of Music
11	Royal Regiment of Fusiliers
12	Westminster Dragoons

FIREPOWER!
THE ROYAL ARTILLERY MUSEUM

Nearest railway station, Woolwich Arsenal. Nearest Underground station, North Woolwich. Bus routes 472, 161, 96, 180 stop in Plumstead Road outside the Royal Arsenal. Bus routes 53, 54, 422, 380 stop in Woolwich town centre

Firepower! The Royal Artillery Museum,
Royal Arsenal, Woolwich, London SE18 6ST
T: 020 8855 7755 F: 020 8855 7100
E: info@firepower.org.uk
www.firepower.org.uk

Curator: Mark Smith

Royal Regiment of Artillery, Royal Artillery, Royal Horse Artillery, Royal Field Artillery, Royal Garrison Artillery, Royal Irish Artillery, Artillery of the Honourable East India Company

Located at Woolwich, the historic home of the regiment since 1716, the museum traces the Regiment's history from that time with a comprehensive display of artillery weapons in a collection of international standing. Alongside the uniforms, guns, medals, badges and other regimental memorabilia are exhibits that enable visitors to feel what it was like to be a 20th century gunner in the ground-shaking field of fire, as the men and women who served in the Royal Artillery tell of their experiences. The science and technology of gunnery is explained with the help of hands-on interactive displays.

Opening Hours: Apr–Oct: Wed–Sun 10.30am–5pm. Nov–Mar: Fri, Sat, Sun 10.30am–5pm

Admission: Adults £5, seniors £4.50, children £2.50, family ticket £12. Groups and school parties by arrangement

Facilities: Parking, restaurant, toilets, lecture room, shop, disabled access, corporate events

GUARDS MUSEUM

Nearest Underground, St James's Park. Access is from Birdcage Walk.

Guards Museum, Wellington Barracks, Birdcage Walk, London SW1E 6HQ
T: 020 7414 3428 F: 020 7414 3429
E: Guardsmuseum@aol.com
www.theguardsmuseum.com

Curator: Andrew Wallis

Grenadier Guards, 1st or Grenadier Regiment of Foot Guards, 1st Regiment of Foot Guards, King's Royal Regiment of Guards, His Majestie's Regiment of Guards (Wentworth's Regiment), Coldstream Guards, Coldstream Regiment of Foot Guards, Lord General's Regiment of Foot Guards, Lord General's Regiment of Foot, General Monck's Regiment (The Coldstreamers), Scots Guards, Scots Fusilier Guards, 3rd Regiment of Foot Guards, Scotch Guards (or Scotts Guards), The King's Lyfe Guards of Foot, The King's Foot Guards, The King's Regiment, His Majestie's Regiment of Guards, Our Regiment of Guards, New Regiment of Foot Guards, Argyll's Regiment of Royal Scotsmen, Irish Guards, Welsh Guards, Guards Camel Regiment, Machine Gun Guards, Guards Machine Gun Regiment, Guards Parachute Company

Uniforms, colours, weapons, silver, medals, pictures and many interesting items of memorabilia illustrating the history of the five regiments of Foot Guards in their service of sovereign and country in times of war and peace. Personal records of members of the Foot Guards are not part of the collection and access to them is not available through the museum.

Opening Hours: Daily 10am–4pm (last admissions 3.30pm). Occasional closures on ceremonial days – please ring to avoid disappointment

Admission: Adults £3, seniors and students £2, children under 16 free. Groups and school parties by arrangement

Facilities: Shop, disabled access, corporate events

HOUSEHOLD CAVALRY MUSEUM

Nearest Underground stations are Charing Cross, Embankment and Westminster

Household Cavalry Museum, Horse Guards, Whitehall, London SW1A 2AX
T: 020 7414 2392 F: 020 7 414 2212
E:museum@householdcavalry.co.uk
www.householdcavalry.co.uk

Director: John Lange

Life Guards, 1st Life Guards, 2nd Life Guards, Horse Grenadier Guards, Blues and Royals (Royal Horse Guards and 1st Dragoons), Royal Horse Guards (The Blues), Royal Horse Guards (Blue), King's or 1st Regiment of Horse, Royal Regiment of Horse (Oxford Blues)

The Household Cavalry Museum collections represent over 300 years of military history, and reflect the unique ceremonial and operational role of the Regiment. These collections are to be re-displayed in a new museum, scheduled to open in June 2007, at Horse Guards. The museum gallery will provide an introduction to the dual role of today's Household Cavalry Regiment and trace its origins and historical development. Visitors will also gain access to the working stable block and see behind the scenes of public duty.

The regimental archive will re-open to the public in December 2007 at Combermere Barracks, Windsor SL2 3DN (Tel: 01753 755194). The archive, library, and education department will form part of a new resource facility that will support the Household Cavalry Museum in London.

Opening Hours: Museum to open in June 2007

Admission: There will be an admission charge. Contact museum for details

Facilities: Museum shop, toilets, disabled access

HONOURABLE ARTILLERY COMPANY MUSEUM 4

Nearest Underground station is Moorgate

Honourable Artillery Company Museum, Armoury House, City Road, London EC1Y 2BQ
T: 020 7382 1537 F: 020 7382 1538
E: hac@hac.org.uk www.hac.uk.com

The finest examples of the Company's extensive collection of uniforms and weapons are displayed in the Museum. The displays include some important early 19th-century shooting medals, reflecting the Company's tradition of excellence in musketry. Service medals are displayed in the Medal Room; the earliest medal sets – all donated by members and their families – date from the Boer War. The VCs won by two members of the Company at Gavrelle in 1917 are proudly displayed in a separate cabinet. The Library, in the Sergeant's Cottage, contains books relating to the Company's history, and warfare in the 19th and 20th centuries. Enquiries to the Archivist are answered by post only and a donation may be requested.

Opening Hours: The museum is currently closed for refurbishment and is expected to re-open in late 2007.

Admission: Free. Donations welcome

Facilities: Toilets, disabled access, corporate events

INNS OF COURT AND CITY YEOMANRY MUSEUM 5

Nearest Underground station is Chancery Lane

Inns of Court and City Yeomanry Museum, 10 Stone Buildings, Lincoln's Inn, London WC2A 3TG
T: 020 7405 8112 F: 020 7414 3496
E: iccy.li@virgin.net

Curator: Denis Durkin

A small collection housed in a classical George II building (1760 approx.) in Lincoln's Inn, recording the most unusual history of the Regiment and its predecessor units. The history stretches back to

1584 when the membership, all lawyers, was formed to defend London against the threat of a Spanish invasion. Subsequently, members took part in the English Civil War and the defence of the City during the Gordon Riots. Units were raised during the Napoleonic Wars and members fought during the Boer War and in later conflicts. It is the only regiment which had (and still has) a very close association with London's legal profession. In addition to uniforms, weapons, medals and memorabilia, there is an excellent archive and possibly the oldest complete set of drums in the British Army, presented to the Law Association Volunteers in 1803.

Opening Hours: Mon–Fri 10am–4pm. By prior appointment only

Admission: Free, donations welcome. Groups and school parties by appointment

Facilities: Toilets. No disabled access

LONDON IRISH RIFLES MUSEUM 6

London bus services 36, 185 and 436. Nearest Underground station is Oval

London Irish Rifles Museum, Connaught House, Flodden Road, Camberwell, London SE5 9LL
T: 020 7820 4046 F: 020 7820 4041
E: museum@londonirishrifles.com
www.londonirishrifles.com

Curator: Captain (Retd) Nigel Wilkinson TD

A small collection of objects, medals and photographs reflecting the history of the Regiment from its foundation in 1859, through subsequent service in South Africa, the Western Front and Palestine in the Great War, as well as in Iraq, North Africa, Sicily and Italy in World War II. Among many other historic documents the collection includes the Roll of Honour from the Great War.

Opening Hours: By appointment only

Admission: Free

All information is correct at the time of going to press, but **you are advised to contact museums before making a visit**

31

LONDON SCOTTISH REGIMENT MUSEUM **7**

Nearest Underground station is St James's Park

London Scottish Regiment Museum,
95 Horseferry Road, London SW1P 2DX
T: 020 7630 1639 F: 020 7233 7909
E: archivistlsregt@aol.com
www.londonscottishregt.org/museum.cfm

Regimental Secretary:
Major Stuart Young TD
Regimental Archivist: Clem Webb

A small but important regimental collection which is comprehensive and well displayed. It includes the medals and uniform of Colonel Robert Ogilby, founder of the Army Museums Ogilby Trust.

Opening Hours: By appointment only with the Regiment on Tue, Wed, and Thu 11.00am–4.00pm

Admission: Free, but donations to the London Scottish Benevolent Fund welcome

Facilities: Toilets, lecture room. Lift available but limited wheelchair access

PRINCESS LOUISE'S KENSINGTON REGIMENT **8**

Nearest railway station is Coulsdon South

**Princess Louise's Kensington
Regiment Display Room**
The TA Centre, Marlpit Lane,
Coulsdon, Surrey CR5 2HD
T: 01737 554023 F: 01737 550298

Curator: Mr Stephen Bland
(Tel: 020 8656 9740)

A small regimental collection that may be viewed by appointment only

ROYAL HOSPITAL MUSEUM **9**

Nearest Underground station is Sloane Square. Buses, 11, 22, 211, 239, 319

Royal Hospital Museum,
Royal Hospital Chelsea,
Royal Hospital Road, London SW3 4SR
T: 020 7881 5203 F: 020 7881 5463
E: info@chelsea-pensioners.org.uk
www.chelsea-pensioners.org.uk

Curator: Jon Nuttall

The home of the world famous Chelsea Pensioner since 1692, the Museum details the history and life of the Royal Hospital and its In-Pensioners together with displays of artefacts, documents, medals, cap badges and uniforms. Recent additions include the Sovereign's Mace and Parade Chair. A large diorama depicts the Royal Hospital and Ranelagh Pleasure gardens as they appeared in 1742.

Opening Hours: Daily 10am–12pm and 2pm–4pm. Sun pm only. Closed Christmas, New Year and Easter

Admission: Free

Facilities: Coach parking for party visits, toilets, shop

ROYAL MILITARY SCHOOL OF MUSIC MUSEUM **10**

Underground to Hounslow East, then by bus along B361 or by car along A316 (next to Twickenham rugby ground)

Royal Military School of Music Museum,
Kneller Hall, Twickenham,
Middlesex TW2 7DU
T: 020 8898 5533 Ext 8652 F: 020 8744 8652
E: corpssec@hq.dcamus.mod.uk

Curator: Major JH Carter

The collection consists mainly of musical instruments used by military bands since 1780, plus uniforms, paintings and associated objects. The archive is housed in the Curator's office and may be viewed by appointment.

Opening Hours: By appointment only

Admission: £3

Facilities: Parking, café, toilets, limited disabled access

SPINK

— FOUNDED 1666 —

The Medals and Militaria Specialists

An Officer's Chapka of the City of London Yeomanry
Sold on 20 July 2006 for £4140

For more information on buying or selling with Spink please contact
The Medals and Militaria Department:
Tel: +44 (0)20 7563 4064 Fax: +44 (0)20 7563 4068
email: cwebb@spink.com

69 Southampton Row, London WC1B 4ET
Tel: +44 (0)20 7563 4000 Fax: +44 (0)20 7563 4066

www.spink.com

LONDON

ROYAL REGIMENT OF FUSILIERS (LONDON) MUSEUM

Nearest Underground station is Tower Hill. Buses 15, 42, 78

Royal Regiment of Fusiliers (London) Museum,
HM Tower of London, London EC3N 4AB
T: 020 7488 5610 F: 020 7481 1093
E: royalfusiliers@fsmail.net

Curator: Major Colin Bowes-Crick

Royal Fusiliers (City of London Regiment), 7th Regiment of Foot (or the Royal Fuziliers), Royal Regiment of Fusiliers (or Ordnance Regiment)

The collection of the Royal Fusiliers (City of London Regiment) covering its history from 1685 to 1968 and of the Royal Regiment of Fusiliers from 1968 onwards. The exhibits include uniforms, weapons, equipment, colours and dioramas of the battles of Albuhera, Mons and Cassino.

Opening Hours: Weekdays 9.30am–5.15pm, Sun 10.30am–5.15pm. Winter close at 4.15pm

Admission: In addition to Tower entry charge: adults £1, children under 12 free

Facilities: Shop

WESTMINSTER DRAGOONS MUSEUM

Nearest Underground station is Putney Bridge

W (Westminster Dragoons) Squadron,
Fulham House, 87 Fulham High Street,
London SW6 3JS
T: 020 7384 4201
E: ry-wsqnpsao@tanet.mod.uk
www.westminsterdragoons.co.uk

Curator: Captain Christopher Sayer

A small private collection relating to the Westminster dragoons. The collection is expected to re-open in early 2007 following refurbishment.

Opening Hours: By appointment only

Admission: Free

TR MILITARY SEARCH

Ancestor Research

Expert research in the records of the British and Indian Armies and their personnel

Miss Elizabeth Talbot-Rice TD
65a Wix's Lane
London SW4 0AH
Tel: 0207.228.5129

East Anglia

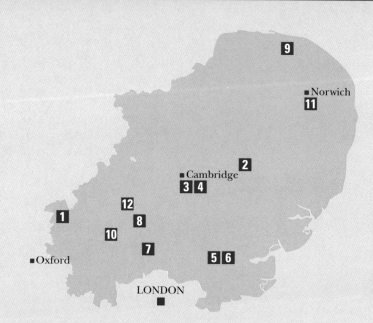

1	Buckingham:	**Buckinghamshire Military Museum**
2	Bury St Edmunds:	**Suffolk Regiment**
3	Cambridge:	**Cambridgeshire Regiment**
4	Cambridge:	**Royal Anglian Regiment**
5	Chelmsford:	**Essex Regiment**
6	Chelmsford:	**Essex Yeomanry**
7	Hertford:	**Hertfordshire Regiment**
8	Hitchin:	**Hertfordshire Yeomanry and Artillery Collection**
9	Holt:	**Suffolk and Norfolk Yeomanry**
10	Luton:	**Bedfordshire and Hertfordshire Regiment**
11	Norwich:	**Royal Norfolk Regiment**
12	Shefford:	**Military Intelligence Museum**

Buckingham

BUCKINGHAMSHIRE MILITARY MUSEUM TRUST

Buckinghamshire Military Museum Trust Collection, The Old Gaol Museum, Market Hill, Buckingham MK18 1JX T: 01280 823020 E: ian.beckett@northampton.ac.uk

Curator: Professor Ian FW Beckett

Royal Bucks King's Own Militia, Royal Buckinghamshire Hussars, Buckinghamshire Rifle Volunteers, Buckinghamshire Territorial Force and Territorial Army Battalions, Bucks Volunteer Training Corps, Buckinghamshire Home Guard

A display of items associated with the auxiliary military forces of Buckinghamshire. The archives are housed separately in the Buckinghamshire County Record Office in Aylesbury.

Opening Hours: Apr–Oct: Mon–Sat 10am–4pm, Sun 2pm–4pm

Admission: Adults £1, seniors/children 50p. Groups/school parties by appointment

Facilities: Refreshments, toilets, shop, lecture room, disabled access

Bury St Edmunds

THE SUFFOLK REGIMENT MUSEUM

Suffolk Regiment Museum, The Keep, Gibraltar Barracks, Newmarket Road, Bury St Edmunds, Suffolk IP33 3RN T: 01603 400290 and 01284 752394 E: taff@taffmail.demon.co.uk www.suffolkregiment.org/Museum.html

Curator: Major AGB Cobbold

Royal Anglian Regiment, The Suffolk Regiment, 12th (or East Suffolk) Regiment of Foot, 12th Regiment of Foot, Duke of Norfolk's Regiment of Foot, Cambridgeshire Regiment TA

Following extensive renovation and refurbishment, the museum re-opened in 2004 and houses a well-presented, comprehensive collection of objects associated with the County Regiment of Suffolk. The collection includes displays of uniforms, weapons, regimental trophies from the Regiment's many campaigns in the service of the Crown, badges, insignia, musical items and other regimental memorabilia. The Regimental Archive is held by the Suffolk County Records Office, Tel 01284 352352.

Opening Hours: 9.30am–3.30pm on the first Wed each month and, during the Summer, on the first Sun of Apr, May, Jun, Jul, Aug and Sep

Admission: Free, donations welcome

Facilities: Parking, toilets

Cambridge

CAMBRIDGESHIRE REGIMENT COLLECTION

As for Royal Anglian Regiment Museum below

The Cambridgeshire Regiment Collection is a small but well presented display of items associated with the County's volunteer infantry regiment. It is housed adjacent to the Royal Anglian Regiment Museum and all details are as shown below.

ROYAL ANGLIAN REGIMENT MUSEUM

By road, leave M11 at J10 or take A505 Royston-Newmarket road. There is a scheduled bus service from Cambridge city centre and railway station, and a daily express coach service from London

Royal Anglian Regiment Museum, Duxford Airfield, Duxford, Cambridge CB2 4QR T: 01223 497298 E: info@royalanglianmuseum.org.uk www.royalanglianmuseum.org.uk

Museum Officer: Andy Murkin

Royal Anglian Regiment, 1st East Anglian Regiment (Royal Norfolk and Suffolk), 2nd East Anglian Regiment (Duchess of Gloucester's Own; Royal Lincolnshire and Northamptonshire), 3rd East Anglian Regiment (16th/44thFoot), Royal Leicestershire Regiment

The collection covers the history of the Royal Anglian Regiment since the amalgamations of the former County Regiments of East Anglia and the East Midlands in 1958-1960. The several amalgamations which preceded today's regiment date back to 1685 and are well illustrated in a detailed family tree. Exhibits include uniforms, weapons, badges and displays dedicated to particular operations on which the egiment has been deployed.

Opening Hours: Summer 10am–6pm daily. Winter 10am–4pm daily

Admission: Free after payment of entrance fee to the Imperial War Museum

Facilities: Parking, refreshments, toilets, lecture room, shop, disabled access

Chelmsford

ESSEX REGIMENT MUSEUM   **5**

SSW of town just off A1016, or buses 152, 154, 350, 351, 42 and 44 from town centre and railway station

Essex Regiment Museum,
Oaklands Park, Moulsham Street,
Chelmsford, Essex CM2 9AQ
T: 01245 605701   F: 01245 262428
E: pompadour@chelmsford.gov.uk
www.chelmsfordbc.gov.uk/
essexregimentmuseum

Curator: Ian Hook

Royal Anglian Regiment, 3rd East Anglian Regiment, Essex Regiment, 44th (or the East Essex) Regiment of Foot, 44th Regiment of Foot, Colonel Long's Regiment of Foot, 56th (or the West Essex) Regiment of Foot, 56th Regiment of Foot, Essex Militia, Rifles, Rifle Volunteer and Volunteer units, Essex Yeomanry Cavalry, Essex Artillery Volunteers, Essex and Suffolk Royal Garrison Artillery, Essex (Fortress) Royal Engineers, Essex Local Defence Volunteers, Essex Home Guard

The regimental collection, housed in an extension to the Chelmsford Museum, is an impressive display of well-presented exhibits tracing the history of the Regiment from 1741 to the present day. Uniforms, trophies – including the Salamanca Eagle captured from the French 62nd Regiment – badges, insignia, weapons and regimental memorabilia reflect the worldwide service of the Essex Regiment in the service of the Crown. Access to a comprehensive family history database is available by appointment, letter or email, for which a donation to The Trustees of the Essex Regiment Museum is appreciated. All details are as shown below.

ESSEX YEOMANRY COLLECTION   **6**

The museum also houses the collection of the Essex Yeomanry whose history and other details are available from their website www.essex-yeomanry.org.uk.

Opening Hours: Mon–Sat 10am–5pm, Sun 2pm–5pm (Winter 1pm–4pm)

Admission: Free. Groups and school parties by appointment

Facilities: Parking, toilets, shop, education service, disabled access

Hertford

HERTFORDSHIRE REGIMENT MUSEUM   **7**

Close to town centre and public parking. Nearest station is Hertford East

Hertfordshire Regiment Museum Collection, Hertford Museum,
18 Bull Plain, Hertford SG14 1DT
T: 01922 582686
E: hertfordmuseum@btconnect.com
www.hertfordmuseum.org

Curator: Helen Gurney

A small regimental collection accessible by appointment at present.

Opening Hours: Tue–Sat 10am–5pm

Admission: Free

Facilities: Toilets, shop

Hitchin

HERTFORDSHIRE YEOMANRY AND ARTILLERY COLLECTION   **8**

Along A505 Hitchin-Luton road or A600 Hitchin-Bedford road

Hertfordshire Yeomanry and Artillery Collection, Hitchin Museum, Paynes Park, Hitchin, Hertfordshire SG5 1EQ
T. 01462 434476   F. 01462 431316
E. david.hodges@north-herts.gov.uk
www.north-herts.gov.uk

Curator: David Hodges

A small collection of uniforms, badges, weapons and medals of the Yeomanry and Artillery units raised in Hertfordshire from 1794 to modern times. The associated archives are held at the Hertfordshire Archives and Local Studies Centre, County Hall, Hertford SG13 8DE:

Opening Hours: Mon–Sat (except Wed) 10am–5pm. Closed Sun, Wed and public holidays

Admission: Free

Facilities: Parking, shop, disabled access

EAST ANGLIA

Holt

SUFFOLK AND NORFOLK YEOMANRY COLLECTION

Off the main A149 coast road four miles west of Sheringham

Suffolk and Norfolk Yeomanry Collection, The Muckleborough Collection, Weybourne, Holt, Norfolk NR25 7EG
T: 01263 588210   F: 01263 588425
E: info@muckleburgh.co.uk
www.muckleburgh.co.uk

Curator: Michael Savory

A small regimental collection within a much larger display of weapons, vehicles and equipment totalling some 3,000 objects.

Opening Hours: Feb–Nov 10am–5pm daily

Admission: Adults £5.50, seniors £4.50, children £3, family £13.50. Groups and school parties by appointment

Facilities: Parking, toilets, shop, disabled access

Luton

BEDFORDSHIRE AND HERTFORDSHIRE REGIMENT MUSEUM

1 mile north of town centre

Bedfordshire and Hertfordshire Regiment Museum Collection, Wardown Museum, Wardown Park, Luton, Bedfordshire LU2 7HA
T: 01582 546722/546725   F: 01582 546763
E: Elizabeth.Adey@luton.gov.uk
www.luton.gov.uk/museums

Curatorial Advisor: Elizabeth Adey

Bedfordshire and Hertfordshire Regiment, Bedfordshire Regiment, 16th (or Bedfordshire) Regiment of Foot, 16th (or Buckinghamshire) Regiment of Foot, 16th Regiment of Foot, Colonel Douglas's Regiment of Foot

Within Wardown Museum, a gallery devoted to the regimental collection of the County Regiment and its predecessors. Bedfordshire and Luton Archives and Records Service, holds the Regimental Archives. For family history enquiries contact Nigel Lutt on 01234 228833, or email Nigel.Lutt@Bedscc.gov.uk

Opening Hours: Tue–Sat: 10am–5pm, Sun 1pm–5pm. Closed 25–26 Dec and 1 Jan

Admissions: Free

Facilities: Parking, refreshments, toilets, shop, disabled access

Norwich

ROYAL NORFOLK REGIMENT MUSEUM

Town centre location on the east side of the Castle Mound

Royal Norfolk Regiment Museum, Shirehall, Market Avenue, Norwich, Norfolk NR1 3JQ
T: 01603 493649   F: 01603 493623
E: regimental.museum@norfolk.gov.uk
www.museums.norfolk.uk

Curator: Kate Thaxton

Royal Anglian Regiment, Royal Norfolk Regiment, Norfolk Regiment 9th (or East Norfolk) Regiment of Foot, 9th Regiment of Foot, Colonel Henry Cornwall's Regiment of Foot

The Regiment was formed in 1685 and served around the world. The museum tells its story and the part that Norfolk's soldiers, and their families, played in shaping three centuries of global history. The displays are themed and arranged chronologically, with excellent interpretative panels; designed for those with no military knowledge as well as the military historian.

Opening Hours: Tue–Fri 10am–4.30pm, Sat 10am–5pm

Admission: Adults £3, concessions £2.50, children £1.60, family ticket £6.50

Facilities: Shop, archives by appointment

Shefford

MILITARY INTELLIGENCE MUSEUM

Off A600 between Bedford and Shefford, sign-posted "Chicksands"

The Military Intelligence Museum, Defence Intelligence and Security Centre, Chicksands, Shefford, Bedfordshire SG17 5PR   T: 01462 752896   F: 01462 752374
E: musarchdint-d@disc.mod.uk

Curator: Mrs Helen O'Hara MA (Hons)

The collections of The Military Intelligence Museum include the Intelligence Corps Museum which charts the development of British Military Intelligence along with the Medmenham Collection highlighting the important role of aerial imagery. Combined with this is the BRIXMIS Collection – telling the story of intelligence gathering in East Germany at the height of the Cold War. Finally there is the story of Chicksands – including its use in World War II as a "Y" Service intercept station of Enigma Codes and its post-war USAF intelligence gathering activities up to the late 1990s. A varied and interesting collection allowing you to "Share the Secret…"

Opening Hours: By appointment only, please contact us

Admission: Free

Facilities: Parking, toilets

Wales

■ Liverpool

2

9

1

6   **5**

8

7

■ Cardiff
3 **4**
Bristol ■

WALES

1	Brecon:	**Royal Regiment of Wales**
2	Caernarfon:	**Royal Welch Fusiliers**
3	Cardiff:	**1st The Queen's Dragoon Guards**
4	Cardiff:	**Museum of the Welch Regiment**
5	Carmarthen:	**Carmarthen Militia and Volunteers**
6	Haverfordwest:	**Pembroke Yeomanry**
7	Monmouth:	**Royal Monmouthshire Royal Engineers (Militia)**
8	Tenby:	**Castlemartin Yeomanry**
9	Welshpool:	**Montgomeryshire Yeomanry**

Brecon

ROYAL REGIMENT OF WALES (BRECON) MUSEUM

By regular bus service from Abergavenny, Newport and Merthyr Tydfil railway stations. Museum is next to Brecon Barracks on B4601

Royal Regiment of Wales (Brecon) Museum, The Barracks, Brecon, Powys LD3 7EB
T: 01874 613310 F: 01874 613275
E: swb@rrw.org.uk
www.rrw.org.uk

Curator: Major Martin Everett

The Royal Welsh, Royal Regiment of Wales (24th/41st Foot), South Wales Borderers, 24th (2nd Warwickshire) Regiment of Foot, 24th Regiment of Foot, Sir Edward Dering's Regiment of Foot, The Monmouthshire Regiment, Brecknockshire, Radnorshire, Montgomeryshire and Monmouthshire Militia and Volunteers Regiments

The regimental collections of the South Wales Borderers and the Monmouthshire Regiment are the focus of well-presented displays in this fine regimental museum. Of particular interest are the exhibits covering the activities of the Regiment in the 1879 Anglo-Zulu War including the 24th's heroic defence of Rorke's Drift. The medal room contains nearly 3,500 medals, and the sixteen Victoria Crosses won by members of the Regiment form an impressive central display. The regimental archive and library are on the same site and may be viewed by appointment with the Curator. Also nearby is the Regimental Chapel in Brecon Cathedral which contains the famous Queen's Colour of the 1/24th saved by Lieutenants Melvill and Coghill after the disaster at Isandlwana in 1879.

Opening Hours: Mon–Fri throughout the year, 10am–5pm. Summer: Sat and bank holidays 10am–4pm. See website or contact the museum for details of special Sunday openings

Admission: Adults £3, children up to the age of 16 are free. Group rates are negotiable. School parties by appointment. School workshops provided

Facilities: Parking, toilets, lecture room, shop, disabled access

Caernarfon

ROYAL WELCH FUSILIERS MUSEUM

A55 from Chester or A487 from South and Mid Wales and follow signs to the museum. By rail to Bangor and then bus or taxi to Caernarfon

Royal Welch Fusiliers Museum, The Castle, Caernarfon, Gwynedd LL55 2AY
T: 01286 673362 F: 01286 677042
E: rwfusiliers@callnetuk.com
www.rwfmuseum.org.uk

Curator: Brian Owen

The Royal Welsh, Royal Welch Fusiliers, Royal Welsh Fusiliers, 23rd Regiment of Foot (Royal Welsh Fusiliers), Royal Regiment of Welsh Fusiliers, Prince of Wales's Own Royal Welsh Fusiliers, Welsh Regiment of Fuziliers, Lord Herbert of Chirbury's Regiment of Foot, Herbert's Regiment, Purcell's Regiment, Morgan's Regiment, Ingoldsby's Regiment, Sabine's Regiment, Peer's Regiment, Huske's Regiment, Denbighshire Hussars Yeomanry, Montgomeryshire Hussars Yeomanry

The collection covers the 300-year history of Wales's oldest infantry regiment and occupies five floors in two towers of the castle. There are fine displays of uniforms, medals and regimental memorabilia from the many campaigns in which it has fought. There is also reference to the Regiment's famous World War I literary heritage linked to Robert Graves, Siegfried Sassoon, David Jones, Frank Richards and Dr Dunn. The regimental library and archive are not held on site and may be viewed by appointment.

Opening Hours: Daily: Spring and Autumn 9.30am–5pm. Summer 9.30am–5.30pm. Winter 11am–4pm. Closed Christmas Eve, Christmas Day, Boxing Day and New Year's Eve

Admission: Free with entry to Caernarfon Castle: adults £4.90, concessions £4.50, family £15

Facilities: Adjacent parking, toilets, shop

WALES

Cardiff

1ST THE QUEEN'S DRAGOON GUARDS MUSEUM 3

City centre location near railway stations, bus services and car parking

1st The Queen's Dragoon Guards Museum, Cardiff Castle, Castle Street, Cardiff, South Glamorgan CF10 2RB
T: 02920 781213 F: 02920 781384
E: curator@qdg.org.uk
www.qdg.org.uk

Curator: Mr Clive Morris

1st Queen's Dragoon Guards, 1st King's Dragoon Guards, 2nd Dragoon Guards (Queen's Bays), 2nd (Queen's) Dragoon Guards, 2nd or Queen's Regiment of Dragoons, 1st or King's Regiment of Dragoon Guards, Queen's or 2nd Regiment of Horse, Queen's Own Royal Regiment of Horse, Princess of Wales's Own Royal Regiment of Horse, King's Regiment of Horse, 2nd Horse, 3rd Regiment of Horse (Peterborough's), Queen's Regiment of Horse

This collection, reflecting the long history of Wales's only regular cavalry regiment, **is temporarily closed** during major renovation and refurbishment of the museum. **Re-opening is anticipated in July/August 2007** and details will be available from the curator or the museum website.

MUSEUM OF THE WELCH REGIMENT (41ST/69TH FOOT) OF THE ROYAL WELSH (23RD/24TH/41ST/69TH FOOT) 4

City centre location near railway stations, bus services and car parking

Museum of the Welch Regiment (41st/69th Foot), Black and Barbican Towers, The Castle, Cardiff, South Glamorgan, CF10 2RB
T: 02920 229367
E: welch@rrw.org.uk
www.rrw.org.uk

Curator: Mr John Dart

Royal Welsh, Royal Regiment of Wales, The Welch Regiment (41st/69th Foot), 41st (The Welsh) Regiment of Foot, 41st Regiment of Foot or Invalids, 41st (Royal Invalids) Regiment, Colonel Fielding's Regiment of Foot, 69th (South Lincolnshire) Regiment of Foot

The collection covers the history of services of the 41st and 69th Regiments of Foot from 1719 until 1969, when The Welch Regiment amalgamated with others to form The Royal Regiment of Wales then in 2006 became The Royal Welsh. The 41st Foot was originally formed of Out-Pensioners from the Royal Hospital Chelsea and titled Sir Edmund Fielding's Regiment of Invalids. In 1787 the title Invalids was abandoned and the 41st became a marching Regiment of The Line. In 1881 it was joined by the 69th Regiment of Foot and became The Welch Regiment.

Opening Hours: Daily (except Tue) 10am–5.30pm

Admission: Included with admission to castle grounds: adults £3.50, children £2.20, seniors £2.70, students £2.95, family ticket £11.40

Facilities: Refreshments, toilets, shop

The museum is expected to close temporarily during a move within Cardiff Castle at a time yet to be determined. Visitors are advised to contact the museum prior to their visit to check opening arrangements.

Carmarthen

CARMARTHEN MILITIA AND VOLUNTEERS COLLECTION 5

Museum located on A40, 1.5 miles east of Carmarthen

Carmarthen Militia and Volunteers Collection, Carmarthen County Museum, Abergwili, Carmarthen, Carmarthenshire SA31 2JG
T: 01267 231696 F: 01267 223830
E: museum@carmarthenshire.gov.uk

Curator: Gavin Evans

A small display of objects associated with the local Yeomanry Cavalry, Militia and Volunteer units

Opening Hours: Mon–Sat 10am–4.30pm

Admission: Free. Groups and school parties by appointment

Facilities: Parking, refreshments, toilets, shop, disabled access, education service

All information is correct at the time of going to press, but **you are advised to contact museums before making a visit**

41

Haverfordwest

PEMBROKE YEOMANRY COLLECTION 6

By car, A40 or M4/A48/A40, then 4 miles north on B4329. By coach or train to Haverfordwest

Pembroke Yeomanry Collection, Scolton Manor Museum, Spittal, Haverfordwest, Pembrokeshire SA62 5QL
T: 01437 731328 F: 01437 731743

Curator: Mark Thomas / Charlotte New

The Collection includes uniforms and accoutrements of the Pembroke Yeomanry, Royal Pembroke Militia, Pembroke Volunteers and associated regiments. Items are not on permanent display but can be viewed by appointment. Archives are held at the Haverfordwest County Record Office. There is also a World War II Gallery.

Opening Hours: Sun–Mon from 1 Apr to 31 Oct; 10.30am–5.30pm

Admission: Adults £2, children £1.50, seniors £1. Groups and school parties by appointment

Facilities: Parking, refreshments, toilets, lecture room, shop

Monmouth

ROYAL MONMOUTHSHIRE ROYAL ENGINEERS (MILITIA) MUSEUM 7

At the highest point of the town, behind Woolworth's. Rail and bus links are poor

Royal Monmouthshire Royal Engineers Museum Collection, Castle and Regimental Museum, The Castle, Monmouth NP25 3BS
T: 01600 772175 F: 01600 711428
E: curator@monmouthcastlemuseum.org.uk
www.monmouthcastlemuseum.org.uk

Curator: Patricia Lynesmith

Royal Monmouthshire Royal Engineers (Militia), Royal Monmouthshire (Light Infantry) Militia

The museum of the Senior Regiment of the Reserve Army – the sole survivor of the Militia – covers the history of the Regiment from its initial mustering in 1539. Displays include uniforms, weapons, insignia, medals, drawings, books and documents. Coverage of the Regiment's recent activities includes exhibits related to operations in Iraq. The Regimental archives may be viewed by appointment.

Opening Hours: Apr–Oct: 2pm–5pm daily. Nov–Mar: 2pm–4pm Sat and Sun

Admission: Free. Donations welcome. Groups and school parties by appointment

Facilities: Sales counter

Tenby

CASTLEMARTIN YEOMANRY COLLECTION 8

Town centre location

Castlemartin Yeomanry Collection, Tenby Museum and Art Gallery, Castle Hill, Tenby, Pembrokeshire SA70 7BP
T: 01834 842809 F: 01834 842809
E: tenbymuseum@hotmail.com

Curator: Dr Mike Brew

Within a general collection of items relating to the local area there is a small collection of objects associated with the Castlemartin Troop of the Pembroke Yeomanry Cavalry and Pembroke Cavalry (Castlemartin) (Hussars). A small display area is devoted to the last invasion of British soil in 1797 when the Regiment accepted the surrender of the French landing force. The Collection is not always on public display but is accessible by appointment. Research facilities are available.

Opening Hours: Summer: 10am–5pm daily. Winter: 10am–5pm Mon–Fri (Last admissions 4.30pm)

Admission: Adults £2.50, children £1.25, family £5.50. Groups and school parties by appointment

Facilities: Toilets, lecture room, shop, education service, disabled access

Welshpool

MONTGOMERYSHIRE YEOMANRY COLLECTION 9

On main road, 5 minutes from the station

Montgomeryshire Yeomanry Museum Collection, Powysland Museum, The Canal Wharf, Welshpool, Powys SY21 7AQ
T: 01938 554656 E: powysland@powys.gov.uk

Curator: Eva Bredsdorff

A small collection of items related to the Montgomeryshire Yeomanry within a local museum of archaeology and social history.

Opening Hours: Summer: weekdays 11am–1pm and 2pm–5pm. Closed Wed; weekends 10am–1pm and 2pm–5pm Winter: Sat only 11am–2pm

Admission: Adults £1, seniors 50p, children free. Groups and school parties by appointment. Powys residents free

Facilities: Disabled access and adjacent parking for disabled visitors

For a detailed map, go to **www.streetmap.co.uk** and type in the post code of the museum

WALES

West Midlands

Nottingham

4

3

2

Birmingham

5 **6**
7

8 **9**

1

W. MIDLANDS

1	Hereford:	**Herefordshire Light Infantry**
2	Lichfield:	**Staffordshire Regiment**
3	Shrewsbury:	**Shropshire Regimental Museum**
4	Stafford:	**Staffordshire Yeomanry**
5	Warwick:	**Queen's Own Hussars**
6	Warwick:	**Royal Regiment of Fusiliers (Royal Warwickshire)**
7	Warwick:	**Warwickshire Yeomanry**
8	Worcester:	**Worcestershire Regiment**
9	Worcester:	**Worcestershire Yeomanry**

Hereford

HEREFORDSHIRE LIGHT INFANTRY MUSEUM

Southeast of the city off the Ledbury road and B4224

Herefordshire Light Infantry Museum,
TA Centre, Harold Street,
Hereford HR1 2QX
T: 01432 359917
E: jameshereford@aol.com

Curator: Major James Hereford

*Herefordshire Light Infantry, Herefordshire Regiment,
Herefordshire Rifle Volunteer Corps, Herefordshire Militia*

A small collection of objects associated with the regiments raised in Herefordshire dating from the Volunteers of the Napoleonic period.

Opening Hours: Mon–Fri 9.30am–4pm. By appointment only

Admission: Free

Facilities: Parking, toilets, disabled access

Lichfield

STAFFORDSHIRE REGIMENT MUSEUM

*On A51 Lichfield-Tamworth road next to Whittington Barracks.
Bus no 765 stops outside*

Staffordshire Regiment Museum,
Whittington Barracks, Lichfield,
Staffordshire WS14 9PY
T: 01543 434394/5 F: 01543 434391
E: curator@staffordshire
regimentmuseum.com
www.army.mod.uk/staffords

Curator: Dr Erik Blakeley FRSA

*Staffordshire Regiment (Prince of Wales's), South Staffordshire
Regiment, 38th (or 1st Staffordshire) Regiment of Foot, 38th
Regiment of Foot, Colonel Lillington's Regiment of Foot, North
Staffordshire Regiment (Prince of Wales's), 64th (or 2nd
Staffordshire) Regiment of Foot, 64th Regiment of Foot, 80th (or
Staffordshire Volunteers) Regiment of Foot, 80th Regiment of Foot,
98th (Prince of Wales's) Regiment of Foot, 98th Regiment of Foot*

The collection tells the story of the Regiment and its forebears from its formation in Lichfield in 1705. It includes uniforms, equipment, medals (8 of the Regiment's 13 VCs are on display), badges and regimental memorabilia. There are special sections covering Militia and Volunteers, the Zulu War, both world wars and the Gulf War. There is a children's hands-on area and outside there are armoured vehicles, two Anderson shelters and a long

section of World War I trench. The Regimental archive and library are on-site and may be viewed by appointment. The Museum runs excellent school visits which are linked to the National Curriculum. Several imaginative military re-enactor events take place at weekends throughout the year including Redcoats, World War I, World War II, even carols in the trenches. The Museum regularly features in the Midlands News.

Opening Hours: Mon–Fri 10am–4.30pm all year. Apr: Remembrance Sunday, Sat, Sun and bank holidays 12.30pm–4.30 pm

Admission: Adults £2, concessions £1.50, children £1

Facilities: Parking, toilets, research facilities, shop, disabled access, picnic area

Shrewsbury

SHROPSHIRE REGIMENTAL MUSEUM

100 yards from main bus and railway stations

Shropshire Regimental Museum Trust,
The Castle, Shrewsbury,
Shropshire SY1 2AT
T: 01743 262292 F: 01743 270023
E: shropsrm@zoom.co.uk
www.lightinfantry.org.uk/regiments/
ksli/shrop_museum.htm

Curator: Peter Duckers

*King's Shropshire Light Infantry, King's (Shropshire Light Infantry),
King's Light Infantry, 53rd (or the Shropshire) Regiment of Foot,
53rd Regiment of Foot, 85th King's Light Infantry, 85th (Bucks
Volunteers) (The King's Light Infantry), 85th (Bucks Volunteers)
(Duke of York's Own Light Infantry), 85th (Bucks Volunteers) (Light
Infantry) Regiment, 85th (Bucks Volunteers) Regiment of Foot,
85th (Westminster Volonties) Regiment of Foot, 85th Light
Infantry Regiment or Royal Volontiers, Crauford's Regiment of
Foot, Shropshire Rifle Volunteers, Shropshire Militia, Shropshire
Royal Horse Artillery, Shropshire Yeomanry, Queen's Own
Mercian Yeomanry*

A very rich collection of artefacts, conventionally displayed on 3 floors in a medieval border castle, covering the history of the King's Shropshire Light Infantry and the County's Artillery, Yeomanry, Militia, Volunteer and Territorial units.

Opening Hours: Main Summer season (Easter–end Sep): Mon–Sat 10am–5pm, Sun 10am–4pm. Oct–20 Dec and mid-Feb–Easter: Tue–Sat 10am–4pm. Closed end Dec–mid-Feb

Admission: Free to Borough residents, all children and students and ex-Shropshire regimental members. Otherwise adults £2.50 and concessions £1.25

Facilities: Toilets, shop, disabled access to both main floors

Stafford

STAFFORDSHIRE YEOMANRY MUSEUM [4]

A 10-minute walk from the station. By car exit M6 at J13 then A449 or J14 then A34

Staffordshire Yeomanry Museum,
The Ancient High House,
Greengate Street, Stafford ST16 2JA
T: 01785 619131
E: jfox@staffordbc.gov.uk
www.stafford.gov.uk

Curator: Lieutenant Colonel DJK German

The collection covers the history of this County Yeomanry Cavalry Regiment from its formation in 1794 to 1945. Special emphasis is laid on the World War II period and the Victorian display contains an excellent collection of uniforms. The Boer War and Great War have individual rooms and throughout there are displays of weapons, medals, pictures, detailed models and audio-visual displays. The museum is designed to appeal to the general public as well as military enthusiasts. Some archives are held on site but the majority are in the County Record Office some 500m away.

Opening Hours: Tue–Sat 10am–4pm

Admission: Free

Facilities: Toilets, shop

Warwick

QUEEN'S OWN HUSSARS MUSEUM [5]

Located in the medieval Lord Leycester Hospital near the city centre. A 15-minute walk from the railway station and close to the bus station

The Queen's Own Hussars Museum,
Lord Leycester Hospital, 60 High Street,
Warwick CV34 4BH
T: and F: 01926 492035
E: qohmuseum@qrh.org.uk
www.qohmuseum.org.uk

Curator: Major PJ Timmons
T: 020 7756 2274
Asst Curator: Miss Gillian Mason (on site)

Queen's Own Hussars, 3rd King's Own Hussars, 3rd King's Own Light Dragoons, 3rd King's Own Regiment of Dragoons, 3rd Regiment of Dragoons, Leveson's Dragoons, Queen Consort's Own Regiment of Dragoons, 7th Queen's Own Hussars, 7th (Queen's Own) Regiment of Hussars, 7th (Queen's Own) Light Dragoons, 7th Queen's Own Regiment of Dragoons, Queen's Own Royal Regiment of Dragoons, Princess of Wales's Own Royal Regiment

of Dragoons, Kerr's Dragoons, Polwarth's Dragoons, Jedburgh's Dragoons, Cunningham's Dragoons

This comprehensive Collection covers the history of the Regiment from its foundation in the late 17th century, with emphasis on both horse and tank warfare. Key events in the Regiment's history, from the early Battles of Dettingen and Waterloo onwards, are vividly recreated through the personal stories of individuals and a mixture of real artefacts, equipment, documentation and weapons.

New displays employ computer technology to illustrate the change-over from horses to tanks, the Regiment's decisive role at the Battle of El Alamein in World War II and its global peace-keeping role to the present. Interactive displays include a state-of-the-art reconstruction of an Afrika Korps Observation Post and events at El Alamein. There are artefacts and uniforms for handling and dressing up, as well as more educational material in family packs for children and adults.

The Regimental archives of the 3rd and the 7th Hussars are held on site and may be viewed by appointment. Please telephone in advance of your intended visit if travelling a long distance as staff may not be on site.

Opening Hours: Tue–Sat 10am–5pm (Summer) or 10am–4pm (Winter)

Admission: Entry to the Lord Leycester Hospital: adults £4.90, concessions £4.40, children £3.90

Facilities: Parking, restaurant, toilets, shop, research facilities. Limited disabled access

THE ROYAL REGIMENT OF FUSILIERS (ROYAL WARWICKSHIRE) MUSEUM [6]

A short distance east of the city centre. Well signposted

The Royal Regiment of Fusiliers (Royal Warwickshire) Museum,
St John's House, Warwick CV34 4NF
T: 01926 491653 F: 01869 257633
E: areasecretary@rrfmuseum
warwick.demon.co.uk
www.warwickfusiliers.co.uk

Curator: Major RG Mills

The Royal Regiment of Fusiliers, The Royal Warwickshire Fusiliers, The Royal Warwickshire Regiment, 6th (The Royal 1st Warwickshire) Regiment of Foot, 6th (or 1st Warwickshire) Regiment of Foot, 6th Regiment of Foot, Colonel Lillington's Regiment of Foot

The museum tells the story of the 6th Foot (Royal Warwickshire Regiment) from its raising in 1674 to The Royal Regiment of Fusiliers today. The story of the "Warwickshire Lads", from Private to Field Marshal, is illustrated with an exciting collection of uniforms, weapons, equipment, badges, medals, pictures, documents and regimental memorabilia. The regimental library and archive are on site and may be viewed by appointment.

Opening Hours: 10am–5pm Tue–Sat and bank holidays. Apr–Sep: Sun 2.30pm–5pm

Admission: Free

Facilities: Parking, toilets, shop. No wheelchair access to first floor

WARWICKSHIRE YEOMANRY MUSEUM 7

Near town centre, opposite Church Road

Warwickshire Yeomanry Museum,
The Court House, Jury Street,
Warwick CV34 4EW
T: 01926 492212
E: wtc.admin@btclick.com

Curator: Mr BW Johnson

The museum covers the history of the Warwickshire Yeomanry from 1794 to 1954 with a collection of uniforms, weapons, memorabilia and an important regimental painting by Lady Butler. The regimental library and archive are held on site and may be viewed by appointment.

Opening Hours: Easter–Sep: Fri, Sat and Sun and bank holidays 10am–4pm or at other times by appointment

Admission: Free

Facilities: Shop, adjacent parking

Worcester

WORCESTERSHIRE REGIMENT MUSEUM 8

Close to city centre at north end of the High Street

Worcestershire Regiment Museum Collection, City Museum and Art Gallery, Foregate Street, Worcester WR1 1DT
T: 01905 354359 F: 01905 353871
E: rhq@wfr.army.mod.uk
www.wfrmuseum.org.uk

Curator: Major RS Prophet

Worcestershire and Sherwood Foresters Regiment, Worcestershire Regiment, 29th (or Worcestershire) Regiment of Foot, 29th Regiment of Foot, Colonel Farrington's Regiment of Foot, 36th (or Herefordshire) Regiment of Foot, 36th Regiment of Foot, Viscount Charlemont's Regiment of Foot, Worcestershire Yeomanry, Worcestershire Artillery, Militia and Volunteer units of the Worcestershire Regiment

This well-presented collection covers the history of the Regiment from its raising in 1694 and that of the Worcestershire and Sherwood Foresters Regiment from 1970 to the present day with displays of uniforms, weapons, badges, medals and regimental memorabilia. The Regimental library and archive are not on site and research enquiries should be addressed to RHQ WFR, Norton Barracks, Worcester WR5 2PA, or via the website address shown above.

Opening Hours: Mon–Fri 9.30am–5.30pm, Sat 9.30pm–5pm

Admission: Free

Facilities: Refreshments, toilets, shop, disabled access. Parking nearby.

WORCESTERSHIRE YEOMANRY MUSEUM COLLECTION 9

T: 01905 25371 F: 01905 616979
E: artgalleryandmuseum@ cityofworcester.gov.uk
www.worcestercitymuseum.org.uk

Curator: Tim Bridges

In the same building is the Worcestershire Yeomanry Museum Collection which covers the history of the County's Yeomanry Cavalry from 1794 up to its amalgamation with the Warwickshire Yeomanry in 1956.

W. MIDLANDS

East Midlands

Sheffield■

4

Nottingham
■ 7 8 9 2

1

5

3

Birmingham■

6

E. MIDLANDS

1	Derby:	9th/12th Royal Lancers and Derbyshire Yeomanry
2	Grantham:	Queen's Royal Lancers
3	Leicester:	Royal Leicestershire Regiment
4	Lincoln:	Royal Lincolnshire Regiment and Lincolnshire Yeomanry
5	Loughborough:	Leicestershire Yeomanry
6	Northampton:	Northamptonshire Regiment and Northamptonshire Yeomanry
7	Nottingham:	South Nottinghamshire Hussars Yeomanry
8	Nottingham:	The Sherwood Foresters
9	Nottingham:	Sherwood Rangers Yeomanry

Derby

9TH/12TH ROYAL LANCERS

and

DERBYSHIRE YEOMANRY MUSEUM

Close to the city centre and attached to the city library

9th/12th Royal Lancers Museum, Derby Museum and Art Gallery, The Strand, Derby, Derbyshire DE1 1BS
T: 01332 716659 F: 01332 716670
E: Mike.Galer@derby.gov.uk
www.derby.gov.uk

Curator: Mike Galer

9th/12th Royal Lancers (Prince of Wales's Own), 9th Queen's Royal Lancers, 9th (Queen's) Lancers, 9th Light Dragoons, 9th Dragoons, Wynne's Dragoons, 12th Royal Lancers (Prince of Wales's), 12th (Prince of Wales's Royal) Lancers, 12th (Prince of Wales's) Light Dragoons, 12th Dragoons, Bowle's Dragoons, Derbyshire Yeomanry

This well-presented collection illustrates the history of the Regiment from the raising of the 9th Lancers in 1715 to the present day. Displays include a re-constructed stable, and exhibits include uniforms, weapons, badges and medals as well as photographic material. A touch-screen computer provides access to the 9th/12th Lancers Museum's archive of men who served in World War I, 1914-1919. Photographs have been included wherever possible. The Derbyshire Yeomanry collection tells the story of the soldiers who served with the Regiment from 1794 until its amalgamation with the Leicestershire Yeomanry in 1956. Access to the archives of both Regiments is available by appointment. The Museum also houses a small display of items related to the Derbyshire Regiment, The Sherwood Foresters and the County's Militia and Volunteer units.

Opening Hours: Mon 11am–5pm, Tue–Sat 10am–5pm, Sun and bank holidays 1pm–4pm

Admission: Free

Facilities: Toilets, shop, disabled access. Nearby parking and cafés

Grantham

QUEEN'S ROYAL LANCERS MUSEUM

The Queen's Royal Lancers Museum is re-locating in 2008. For information about the move and new location contact:

Home Headquarters, The Queen's Royal Lancers, Lancer House, Prince William of Gloucester Barracks, Grantham, Lincolnshire NG31 7TJ
T: 0115 9573295
E: qrlmuseum@btinternet.com
www.qrl.uk.com

Curator: Captain JM Holtby

The Queen's Royal Lancers, 16th/5th Queen's Royal Lancers, 16th Queen's Lancers, 16th (Queen's) Light Dragoons, 16th Light Dragoons (Burgoyne's Light Horse), 5th Royal Irish Lancers, 5th (Royal Irish) Lancers, 5th (Royal Irish) Dragoons, 17th/21st Lancers, 17th (Duke of Cambridge's Own) Lancers, 17th Lancers, 17th Light Dragoons, 21st (Empress of India's) Lancers, 21st Hussars, 21st Light Dragoons, Bengal European Cavalry (Honourable East India Company)

The regimental collections of the Queen's Royal Lancers and its immediate antecedent regiments – the 16th/5th Lancers and the 17th/21st Lancers – currently housed in the historic setting of Belvoir Castle, include fine displays of uniforms, weapons, medals, badges, silver and paintings tracing the Regiment's history from Marlborough's campaign to the Gulf War. A touch screen computer gives access to an archive of soldiers who have served with the Regiments. The regimental archive is held at Lancer House (see above) and may be viewed by appointment.

Belvoir Castle – 2007 opening times, dates and prices
Opening Hours: Apr–Sep: 11am–5pm last entry 4pm, Sat 11am–4pm last entry 3pm. Apr open from Tue 3 until Thu 12 and weekends; May and Jun closed Mon and Fri but open bank hols; Jul and Aug closed Fri only; Sep open Sat and Sun only

Admission: Adults £11, students/senior citizens £10, children (5–16) £6, family (2 adults + 3 children) £30

Facilities: Car parking (£1 per car)

E. MIDLANDS

For a detailed map, go to **www.streetmap.co.uk** and type in the post code of the museum

Leicester

ROYAL LEICESTERSHIRE REGIMENT MUSEUM ▪3

West of the main shopping area and east of the river, the museum is easily accessible by foot from the city centre

Royal Leicestershire Regiment Museum Collection,
Newarke Houses Museum, The Newarke,
Leicester LE2 7BY
T: 0116 2254980 F: 0116 2254982
E: museums@leicester.gov.uk
www.leicester.gov.uk/museums

Curator: Mr Philip French

Royal Leicestershire Regiment, Leicestershire Regiment, 17th (or Leicestershire) Regiment of Foot, 17th Regiment of Foot, Colonel Richard's Regiment of Foot

The regimental collection has recently moved into dedicated galleries in the refurbished Newarke Houses Museum. It illustrates the history of the Regiment from 1688 to 1964 when it became part of what is now the Royal Anglian Regiment. Displays include uniforms, medals, regimental memorabilia, photographs, video and interactive family history. They address topics such as recruiting and army life.

Opening Hours: Following extensive refurbishment, the museum will re-open in early 2007, when opening hours are expected to be: Mon–Sat 10am–5pm, Sun 11am–5pm. Closed Dec 24, 25, 26 and 31, and Jan 1

Admission: Free

Facilities: Toilets, disabled access

Lincoln

ROYAL LINCOLNSHIRE REGIMENT ▪4

and

LINCOLNSHIRE YEOMANRY COLLECTIONS

Located on the B1398, 0.5 miles northwest of the Cathedral. City Bus no 1

Royal Lincolnshire Regiment Museum Collection, Museum of Lincoln Life,
Burton Road, Lincoln LN1 3LY
T: 01522 528448 F: 01522 521264
E: steve.rowan@lincolnshire.gov.uk
www.lincolnshire.gov.uk

Keeper of Military Collections: Steve Rowan

Royal Anglian Regiment, Royal Lincolnshire Regiment, Lincolnshire Regiment, 10th (or North Lincolnshire) Regiment of Foot, 10th Regiment of Foot, Earl of Bath's Regiment of Foot, Lincolnshire Yeomanry

The Collections of the Royal Lincolnshire Regiment and the Lincolnshire Yeomanry, now in the care of Lincolnshire County Council, are housed in a listed barracks which was built in 1857 for the Royal Lincoln Militia. The displays of uniforms, weapons, badges, medals and regimental memorabilia cover the history of the County Infantry Regiment from 1685 onwards. Exhibits illustrate the Regiment's service in the American War of Independence, the Sudan campaign, the Boer War and both world wars. A separate display is devoted to uniforms, medals and photographs of the Lincolnshire Yeomanry.

Opening Hours: Apr–Sep: 10am–5pm daily. Oct–Mar: 10am–5pm Mon–Sat. Last admissions 4pm. Closed Dec 24, 25, 26 and 31 and Jan 1

Admission: Adults £2.15, concessions £1.45, children 0–5 free, family £5.75

Facilities: Parking, tearoom, toilets, shop, audio guide, disabled access

Loughborough

LEICESTERSHIRE YEOMANRY MUSEUM COLLECTION ▪5

Town centre location

Leicestershire Yeomanry Museum Collection,
The War Memorial Museum, Queen's Park,
Loughborough, Leicestershire LE11 2TT
T: 01509 231667 F: 01509 634839
E: carillonmuseum@tiscali.co.uk

Archivist: Mrs Pauline Cutter

The Leicestershire Yeomanry Collection is displayed on the first floor of this museum which otherwise contains objects from a number of British and Allied WW2 units of all three Services. Postal inquiries should be addressed to the Chairman of the Trust, Mr Peter Crooks, c/o John Storer House, Wards End, Loughborough, Leicestershire LE11 2HA

Opening Hours: Good Fri–Sep: Mon–Wed and Fri 1pm–4.30pm, Thu and Sat 10am–4.30pm, Sun 1–4.30pm

Admission: Adults 50p, seniors and children free

Facilities: Café and toilets nearby (150m), shop, partial wheelchair access. Disabled parking and drop-off point

All information is correct at the time of going to press, but **you are advised to contact museums before making a visit**

49

E. MIDLANDS

Northampton

NORTHAMPTONSHIRE REGIMENT

and

NORTHAMPTONSHIRE YEOMANRY COLLECTIONS

On the outskirts of town, off the A4500 Wellingborough Road

Northamptonshire Regiment and Northamptonshire Yeomanry Collections, Abington Museum, Abington Park, Northampton NN1 5LW
T: 01604 838110 F: 01604 830720
E: abingtonmuseum@northampton.gov.uk
www.northampton.gov.uk/museums

Cultural Development Team Leader: Peter Field

Royal Anglian Regiment, Northamptonshire Regiment, 48th (or the Northamptonshire) Regiment of Foot, 48th Regiment of Foot, Colonel Cholmondley's Regiment of Foot, 58th (or the Rutlandshire) Regiment of Foot, 58th Regiment of Foot raised by Colonel Robert Anstruther as 60th Foot, Northamptonshire Yeomanry

The regimental collection traces the history of the County Regiment from its formation in 1741 to its amalgamation in 1960. Items include uniforms, prints, pictures, silver, medals and other items of regimental significance. Uniforms and medals form the core of the Yeomanry Collection. Records relating to The Northamptonshire Regiment can be seen by appointment (telephone 01604 83780. The Yeomanry archives are held at the County Record Office (01604 762129).

Opening Hours: Mar–Oct: 1pm–5pm. Nov–Feb: 1pm–4pm, bank holiday Mondays 1–5pm

Admission: Free

Facilities: Toilets, disabled toilet and access to ground floor, baby changing facilities. Parking nearby

Nottingham

SOUTH NOTTINGHAMSHIRE HUSSARS YEOMANRY MUSEUM

South Nottinghamshire Hussars Yeomanry Museum, The TA Centre, Hucknall Lane, Bulwell, Nottingham NG6 8AQ
T: 0115 9272251 E: 100regtra-307btypsao@tanet.mod.uk

Curator: Mr Gil Aldridge

A small regimental collection which may be viewed by appointment only.

THE SHERWOOD FORESTERS (NOTTS AND DERBY REGIMENT) COLLECTION

Close to the city centre and railway station

The Sherwood Foresters (Notts and Derby Regiment) Collection, The Castle, Nottingham NG1 6EL
T: 0115 9465415 F: 0115 9469853
E: rhqwfr-nottm@lineone.net
www.wfrmuseum.org.uk

Curator: Major JOM Hackett

Worcestershire and Sherwood Foresters Regiment, Sherwood Foresters (Nottinghamshire and Derbyshire Regiment), Sherwood Foresters (Derbyshire Regiment), Derbyshire Regiment (Sherwood Foresters), 45th (Nottinghamshire Regiment) Sherwood Foresters, 45th (1st Nottinghamshire) Regiment, Robin Hood Volunteer Rifle Company, 45th Regiment of Foot, 95th (Derbyshire) Regiment of Foot, 95th Regiment of Foot

Displays cover the history of the Regiment from 1741 through its amalgamation with the Worcestershire Regiment in 1970 to recent operations. Objects on display include many of the Regiment's colours, uniforms, head-dress, badges, medals. A touch screen computer gives access to an archive of soldiers who have served with the Regiment. The Archives are held at Chetwynd Barracks, Chilwell, and are accessible by appointment only by telephoning 0115 9465415.

There is also a display in Derby City Museum and Art Gallery shared with the 9th/12th Royal Lancers and the Derbyshire Yeomanry.

Opening Hours: Mar–Sep: daily 10am–5pm. Oct–Feb: daily 11am–4pm. Closed Christmas Day, Boxing Day and New Year's Day

Admission: Adults £3, concessions and children £1.50

Facilities: Refreshments, toilets, shop, disabled access

SHERWOOD RANGERS YEOMANRY MUSEUM

East of Nottingham just off the B686

Sherwood Rangers Yeomanry Museum, S (SRY) Sqn The Royal Yeomanry, Cavendish Drive, Carlton, Nottinghamshire NG4 3DX
T: 0115 9618722 www.sherwood-rangers.org

A small regimental collection which is open to the public by appointment only. Contact should be made through the Chairman of the Old Comrades Association, Mr L Mellors by telephoning 0115 9521909.

For a detailed map, go to **www.streetmap.co.uk** and type in the post code of the museum

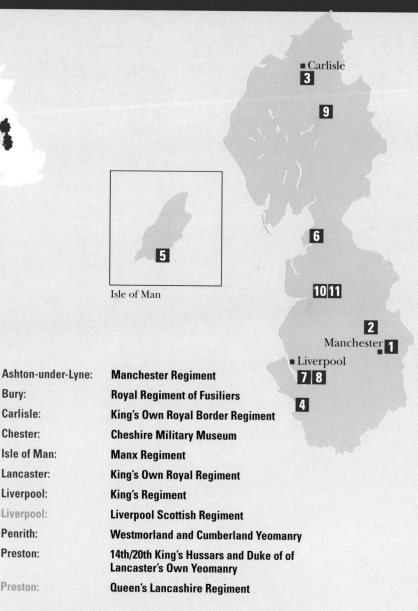

Isle of Man

1	Ashton-under-Lyne:	Manchester Regiment
2	Bury:	Royal Regiment of Fusiliers
3	Carlisle:	King's Own Royal Border Regiment
4	Chester:	Cheshire Military Museum
5	Isle of Man:	Manx Regiment
6	Lancaster:	King's Own Royal Regiment
7	Liverpool:	King's Regiment
8	Liverpool:	Liverpool Scottish Regiment
9	Penrith:	Westmorland and Cumberland Yeomanry
10	Preston:	14th/20th King's Hussars and Duke of of Lancaster's Own Yeomanry
11	Preston:	Queen's Lancashire Regiment

Ashton-under-Lyne

MANCHESTER REGIMENT MUSEUM **1**

P 🚶 ♿ 📷 ♿ 🎦

In the town centre near railway and bus stations and car park

Manchester Regiment Museum, Town Hall, Market Place, Ashton-under-Lyne, Tameside OL6 6DL
T: 0161 3422254 F: 0161 3432869
E: museum.manchesters@tameside.gov.uk
www.tameside.gov.uk

Curator: Garry Smith

Manchester Regiment, 63rd (or the West Suffolk) Regiment of Foot, 63rd Regiment of Foot (Colonel Robert Armiger), 2nd Bn of the 8th (The King's) Regiment of Foot, 96th Regiment of Foot, 96th (Queen's Own) Regiment of Foot, 96th Regiment of Foot (raised as 2nd Bn 52nd Foot), 96th (The Queen's Royal Irish) Regiment, 96th (British Musketeers) Regiment, 96th Regiment of Foot

The collection covers the history of the Regiment from the raising of the 2nd Bn 8th Foot in 1756, through the formation of the Manchester Regiment in 1881 to that Regiment's amalgamation to form The King's Regiment in 1958. Its history is illustrated in the context of the local community from which it stemmed and the social history section covers topics such as women in wartime, war poets, the Spanish Civil War, the Home Guard and National Service. There are displays of uniforms, weapons, medals, badges and regimental memorabilia related to its major campaigns in the American War of Independence, the Crimea, South Africa, both world wars, Palestine and Malaya. The regimental archives are available for researchers at the Local Studies and Archives Library based in Ashton-under-Lyne. (Tel 0161 3424242).

Opening Hours: Mon–Sat 10am–4pm

Admission: Free. Groups and school parties by appointment

Facilities: Toilets, shop, lecture room, disabled access. Adjacent parking

Bury

ROYAL REGIMENT OF FUSILIERS (LANCASHIRE) MUSEUM **2**

P 🚶 ♿ 📷 🎦

By bus from the station to the barracks or by car along A58 Bolton Road 1 mile north of town centre

Royal Regiment of Fusiliers (Lancashire) Museum, Wellington Barracks, Bolton Road, Bury, Lancashire BL8 2PL
T: 0161 7642208 F: 0161 7642208
E: fusilierslancshq@btinternet.com
www.fusiliersmuseum-lancashire.org.uk

Curator: Lt Col Mike Glover

Royal Regiment of Fusiliers, Lancashire Fusiliers, 20th (or East Devonshire) Regiment of Foot, 20th Regiment of Foot, Colonel Sir Robert Peyton's Companies of Foot

The Fusilier Collection in Bury tells the exciting story of one of Lancashire's most famous regiments: The Regiment of 6 VCs before breakfast at Gallipoli – indeed the Regiment that earned more VCs in World War I than any other infantry regiment in the British Army. The archive and displays illustrate the stories of famous members of the Regiment from Wolfe storming Quebec and Ross burning the White House, to the Regiment's connection with Napoleon and Tolkien and the creation of *The Lord of the Rings*. The regimental library and archive are on site and may be viewed by appointment.

Opening Hours: Tue–Sat 10am–4pm

Admission: Free. Groups/school parties by appointment

Facilities: Parking, toilets, lecture room, shop

Note: The museum is planning to move to prestigious new premises in Broad Street, Bury in 2008. Details of the new arrangements and the timing of the move are available from the museum website or by contacting the museum itself.

NORTH WEST

For a detailed map, go to **www.streetmap.co.uk** and type in the post code of the museum

Carlisle

BORDER REGIMENT AND KING'S OWN ROYAL BORDER REGIMENT MUSEUM

North side of city centre, a 15-minute walk from station. By car, exit M6 at J43 or 44

Border Regiment and King's Own Royal Border Regiment Museum, Queen Mary's Tower, The Castle, Carlisle, Cumbria CA3 8UR T: 01228 532774 F: 01228 545435 E: borderregiment@aol.com and korbrmuseum@aol.com

Curator: Stuart Eastwood
Assistant Curator: Tony Goddard

Duke of Lancaster's Regiment (King's, Lancashire and Border), King's Own Royal Border Regiment, Border Regiment, 34th (Cumberland) Regiment of Foot, 34th Regiment of Foot, Lord Lucas's Regiment of Foot, 55th (Westmoreland) Regiment of Foot, 55th Regiment of Foot, 57th Regiment of Foot (Colonel George Perry), Royal Cumberland Militia, Cumberland Militia, Royal Westmorland Light Infantry Militia, Westmorland Militia, Cumberland and Westmorland Rifle Volunteers, Cumberland Artillery

Located within the Inner Ward of Carlisle Castle, the Museum relates the history of Cumbria's County Infantry Regiment, the Border Regiment (34th and 55th Foot) and its successor The King's Own Royal Border Regiment, local Militia, Volunteer and Territorial Army units from 1702 to the present day. Wide-ranging displays on two floors include uniforms, weapons, equipment, medals, silver, pictures, memorabilia, a World War I trench scene and dioramas.

The Castle, founded in 1092, is a superb medieval fortress owned by the Crown and maintained by English Heritage. It can boast almost continuous military occupation for 900 years and preserved within its walls are the 19th-century barracks and military buildings used by The Border Regimental Depot from 1873 to 1959.

Opening Hours: Apr–Sep: 9.30am–5pm daily. Nov–Mar: 10am–4pm daily. Closed 24–26 Dec and 1 Jan

Admission: Included in entry charge to Castle: adults £4.10, concessions £3.10, children (under 16) £2.10, under 5s free, carer with disabled free, 15% discount for groups of 10+. Educational visits in term time free, but must be booked with English Heritage on 01228 591922 or www.english-heritage.org.uk

Facilities: Research service with access to the regimental archives available by appointment. Education Service provided. Guided tours by arrangement. Toilets (including disabled), lecture room, shop, disabled access to ground floor, picnic area, disabled parking at the Castle, other parking nearby

Chester

CHESHIRE MILITARY MUSEUM

Follow signs to the castle from city centre

Cheshire Military Museum, The Castle, Chester, Cheshire CH1 2DN
T: 01244 327617 F: 01244 401700
E: museum@chester.ac.uk
www.chester.ac.uk/militarymuseum

Curator: Major Nigel Hine

22nd (Cheshire) Regiment (The 1st Battalion the Mercian Regiment (Cheshire)), Cheshire Regiment (22nd Foot), 22nd (or the Cheshire) Regiment of Foot, 22nd Regiment of Foot, Duke of Norfolk's Regiment of Foot, Cheshire Yeomanry. Representative collections of 3rd Carabiniers, 5th Inniskilling Dragoon Guards and Eaton Hall Officer Cadet School

An innovative and attractive museum relating the story of the men of the regiments of Cheshire, their families and their community. This 300-year history is told through art, artefacts and memorabilia including fine displays of uniforms, medals and weapons. Access to the archives is available by appointment.

Opening Hours: Daily 10am–5pm (door closes 4.30pm). Closed for two weeks over Christmas

Admission: Adults £2, seniors and children £1, groups and school parties by appointment

Facilities: Shop, lecture room, disabled access and toilets. Parking available in nearby Chester city car parks

Isle of Man

MUSEUM OF THE MANX REGIMENT

To the right of the airport on the road between Ballasalla and Castletown

Museum of the Manx Regiment, Ronaldsway Airport, Ballasalla, Isle of Man T: 01624 829294
E: ivor.ramsden@gov.im
Director: Ivor Ramsden
15th (I.O.M.)Light A.A., Regiment, R.A. (T.A.)

Now redesigned and co-located with the Manx Aviation and Military Museum at the Island's airport, the Manx Regiment Museum commemorates the part played by the Island's Regiment during World War II in the defence of southern England and in overseas theatres such as Egypt, Eritrea, Crete, Italy, France, Holland and Germany. The collection is rich in regimental

All information is correct at the time of going to press, but **you are advised to contact museums before making a visit**

53

NORTH WEST

memorabilia and includes a 40mm Bofors anti-aircraft gun.

Opening Hours: Sat, Sun and bank holidays 10am–4.30pm. Groups and school parties at other times by appointment

Admission: Free

Facilities: Parking, toilets, shop, disabled access

Lancaster

KING'S OWN ROYAL REGIMENT 6

Located in pedestrian City centre a 5-minute walk from railway station. By road: A6, M6 (J33 South or J34 North)

King's Own Royal Regiment Museum,
City Museum, Market Square, Lancaster,
Lancashire LA1 1HT
T: 01524 555619 or 01524 64637
F: 01524 841692
E: kingsownmuseum@iname.com
www.kingsownmuseum.plus.co.uk

Curator: Peter Donnelly

King's Own Royal Border Regiment, King's Own (Royal Lancaster) Regiment, King's Own Royal Regiment (Lancaster), King's Own (Royal Lancaster) Regiment, 4th (The King's Own Royal) Regiment of Foot, 4th (or King's Own) Regiment of Foot, King's Own Regiment of Foot, Queen's Marines, Queen's Own Regiment of Foot, Queen Consort's Regiment, Queen's Regiment, Duchess of York and Albany's Regiment, Earl of Plymouth's Regiment for Tangier (2nd Tangier Regiment), 1st Royal Lancashire Militia.

The museum, housed in the old Town Hall of 1783, was the first municipal museum to include a regimental museum. It tells the story of the King's Own Royal Regiment from 1680 to the present day. Topics covered include the Napoleonic campaigns, the Crimean War, the expedition to Abyssinia, both world wars and subsequent operations and events in which the regiment has participated. Displays include a social history of soldiers who served in the Regiment. There is extensive archive material which is accessible by appointment.

Opening Hours: Mon–Sat 10am–5pm. Closed Christmas and New Year

Admission: Free. Groups and school parties by appointment

Facilities: Shop, lecture room, research facilities, disabled access. Parking nearby

Liverpool

KING'S REGIMENT MUSEUM 7

Pier head, next to Albert Dock

King's Regiment Museum Collection,
Museum of Liverpool Life, Pier Head,
Liverpool L3 1PZ
T: 0151 4784065 F: 0151 4784090
E: matthew.buck@liverpoolmuseums.org.uk
www.army.mod.uk/lancs

Curator: Matthew Buck

King's Regiment (Manchester and Liverpool), King's Regiment (Liverpool), King's (Liverpool Regiment), 8th (or the King's) Regiment of Foot, King's Regiment of Foot, Queen's Regiment of Foot (or Webb's Regiment), Princess Anne of Denmark's Regiment of Foot

The Museum of Liverpool Life and the King's Regiment Museum closed on 4th June 2006.   A new museum is being built on the site and will re-open in early 2009.   It will house new displays of the King's Regiment.   Until then some of the artefacts will be on display at temporary exhibitions through the city.   As details of these become known they will be published on the Museum's website at www.liverpoolmuseums.org.uk/about/capitalprojects/museumofliverpool.asp

Archive enquiries should be sent to the Regimental Headquarters at rhq@kings.army.mod.uk

LIVERPOOL SCOTTISH REGIMENTAL MUSEUM 8

1 mile east of city centre. Off B5178 near Wavertree Park

Liverpool Scottish Regimental Museum,
Forbes House, 139 Botanic Road,
Liverpool (no mail to this address)
T: 01925 766157 or 0151 645 5717 or
07952 2169285
E: ilriley@liverpoolscottish.org.uk
www.liverpoolscottish.org.uk

Curator: Mr Dennis Reeves

Hon Secretary: Major IL Riley TD FSA Scot

19th Lancashire Rifle Volunteers (Liverpool Lowland Volunteers), 71st Lancashire Rifle Volunteers (Liverpool Highland Volunteers), 8th (Scottish) Volunteer Bn King's Liverpool Regiment, 10th (Scottish) Bn King's (Liverpool Regiment TF), 1st and 2nd Bns The Liverpool Scottish Queen's Own Cameron Highlanders, 89th Anti-Tank Regiment Royal Artillery, 655th Light Anti-Aircraft Regiment Royal Artillery, "V" (The Liverpool Scottish) Company 1st Bn Highland Volunteers, "V" (Liverpool Scottish) Company

5th/8th(Volunteer) Bn, The King's Regiment and successor sub-units in the King's and Cheshire Regiment and the Duke of Lancaster's Regiment

This rich collection of regimental artefacts offers a comprehensive representation of the life of a territorial infantry battalion over the last hundred years. There is also extensive archive material including diaries, scrapbooks and records of a significant number of soldiers who have served with the Regiment together with a database of soldiers who served and also of all Merseyside War Memorials.

The address for postal contact with the museum is: Major IL Riley, 51a Common Lane, Culcheth, Warrington WA3 4EY

Opening Hours: Wed 2pm–7pm (phone to confirm) or by appointment

Admission: Free, donations welcome. Groups and school parties by appointment

Facilities: Parking (on road), toilets, lecture room

Penrith

WESTMORLAND AND CUMBERLAND YEOMANRY MUSEUM [9]

On the A592 Penrith to Ullswater road

Westmorland and Cumberland Yeomanry Museum, Dalemain Historic House and Gardens, near Penrith, Cumbria CA11 0HB
T: 01768 486450 F: 01768 486223
E: admin@dalemain.com
www.dalemain.com

Curator: Mr RB Hassell-McCosh

Located in the base of the Norman pele tower, the museum contains many mementoes and relics of the Westmorland and Cumberland Yeomanry as well as the two volunteer forces that preceded it – the Westmorland East and West Wards Local Militia and Cumberland Loyal Leath Ward Volunteers. The displays trace the Regiment's history with particular reference to the Boer War and its role in the Great War as Divisional Cavalry with Kitchener's Army in France.

Opening Hours: Easter–Oct: Sun–Thu 11am–4pm

Admission: Charged. Groups and school parties by appointment

Facilities: Parking, toilets, shop

Preston

14TH/20TH KING'S HUSSARS MUSEUM COLLECTION [10]

and

DUKE OF LANCASTER'S OWN YEOMANRY MUSEUM COLLECTION

Within 400 yards of the bus station on ring road near the junction with Church Street

Museum of Lancashire, Stanley Street, Preston, Lancashire PR1 4YP
T: 01772 264075 F: 01772 264079
www.lancashire.gov.uk

Curator: Dr Stephen Bull

King's Royal Hussars, 14th/20th King's Hussars, 14th (King's) Hussars, 14th (King's) Light Dragoons, 14th (Duchess of York's Own) Light Dragoons, 14th Light Dragoons, 14th Dragoons, 14th Hussars, 20th Hussars, 2nd Bengal European Light Cavalry (Honourable East India Company), Duke of Lancaster's Own Yeomanry, Representative collections of Lancashire Regiments, Loan collection of Queen's Lancashire Regiment

The Museum of Lancashire contains displays relating to several of the county's historic regiments. The gallery of the 14th/20th King's Hussars traces the history of the Regiment from 1715 and includes two Victoria Crosses, a display of guidons and artefacts from the Napoleonic era, India and South Africa. The Duke of Lancaster's Own Yeomanry's 200-year association with Lancashire is portrayed with exhibits from Peterloo, South Africa and WW1. There is also a gallery of Queen's Lancashire Regiment material, a Lancashire Home Front display and a trench scene.

Opening hours: 10.30am–5pm. Closed Thu, Sun and bank holidays

Admission: Adults £3, concessions £2, accompanied children free. Groups and school parties by appointment

Facilities: Parking, refreshments, toilets, lecture room, shop, disabled access

NORTH WEST

All information is correct at the time of going to press, but **you are advised to contact museums before making a visit**

55

QUEEN'S LANCASHIRE REGIMENT MUSEUM

2 miles northeast of town centre on A6063 then B6241

Queen's Lancashire Regiment Museum,
Fulwood Barracks, Watling Street Road,
Preston, Lancashire PR2 8AA
T: 01772 260362 F: 01772 260583
E: qlrmuseum@btconnect.com
www.army.mod.uk/lancs/index.htm

Curator: Miss Jane Davies

The Duke of Lancaster's Regiment, The Queen's Lancashire Regiment, The East Lancashire Regiment: 30th and 59th Foot, The South Lancashire Regiment (Prince of Wales's Volunteers): 40th and 82nd Foot, The Loyal Regiment (North Lancashire): 47th and 81st Foot, The Lancashire Regiment (Prince of Wales's Volunteers)

The museum houses the largest military collection in the North West. It covers the history of the County's three infantry regiments from the raising of Lord Castleton's Regiment of Foot in 1689 through the several amalgamations that have resulted in the creation of the current Duke of Lancaster's Regiment. Objects related to the County's Militia, Rifle Volunteers, Territorial Army, Home Guard and Cadet Units are also on display. The collection, archive and library hold extensive historical material including uniforms, badges, medals, weapons and equipment as well as photographs, film and sound, ceramics and fine and decorative art.

Opening Hours: Tue–Thu 9am–4pm or by appointment

Admission: Free. Groups and school parties by appointment

Facilities: Parking, toilets, lecture room, shop. Adjacent pubs/cafés

NORTH WEST

For a detailed map, go to **www.streetmap.co.uk** and type in the post code of the museum

Yorkshire

1	Barnsley:	**13th/18th Royal Hussars and Light Dragoons**
2	Doncaster:	**King's Own Yorkshire Light Infantry**
3	Halifax:	**Duke of Wellington's Regiment**
4	Hull:	**4th Bn East Yorkshire Regiment**
5	Richmond:	**Green Howards**
6	Rotherham:	**York and Lancaster Regiment**
7	York:	**Kohima Museum**
8	York:	**Prince of Wales's Own Regiment of Yorkshire**
9	York:	**Queen's Own Yorkshire Yeomanry**
10	York:	**Royal Dragoon Guards**

Barnsley

13TH/18TH ROYAL HUSSARS
(QUEEN MARY'S OWN)

and

THE LIGHT DRAGOONS MUSEUM

Bus 236 (Huddersfield), along A635 and A637 roads to Cawthorne and Kexbrough

13th/18th Royal Hussars (QMO) and Light Dragoons Museum,
Cannon Hall, Cawthorne, Barnsley,
South Yorkshire S75 4AT
T: 01226 790270 F: 01226 792117
E: mail@lightdragoons.org.uk
www.lightdragoons.org.uk/
regimental_history/cannonhall.php

Curator: Captain GE Locker

The Light Dragoons, 13th/18th Royal Hussars, 13th Hussars, 13th Light Dragoons, 18th Royal Hussars (Queen Mary's Own), 18th Light Dragoons

The Collection covers the history of the 13th/18th Royal Hussars with a series of displays illustrating the life of the Regiment in peace and war from 1715 to the present time. Exhibits relate to the Battle of Waterloo, Charge of the Light Brigade, Boer War, both world wars and The Light Dragoons' involvement in recent UN and NATO operations.

Opening Hours: Apr–Oct: Wed–Fri 10.30am–5pm, Sat/Sun 12pm–5pm. Nov, Dec and Mar: Sun only 12pm–4pm. Closed Jan and Feb

Admission: Free

Facilities: Parking, refreshments, toilets, lecture room, shop, education service, corporate events

Doncaster

KING'S OWN YORKSHIRE LIGHT
INFANTRY MUSEUM

Close to Doncaster town centre, off Waterdale

King's Own Yorkshire Light Infantry Museum, Doncaster Museum and Art Gallery, Chequer Road, Doncaster, South Yorkshire DN1 2AE
T: 01302 734293 F: 01302 735409
E: museum@doncaster.gov.uk
www.doncaster.gov.uk/museums

Curator: Mr Geoff Preece

King's Own Yorkshire Light Infantry, 51st (2nd Yorkshire West Riding), 105th (Madras Light Infantry)

An excellent collection of regimental memorabilia, uniforms, pictures and silver, dating from the raising of the Regiment in 1755 to its amalgamation into the Light Infantry in 1968. It includes an extensive medal collection. The regimental archive is held in Pontefract (Tel: 01977 703181) and access is by appointment only with Major CMJ Deedes

Opening Hours: Mon–Sat 10am–5pm, Sun 2–5pm

Admission: Free

Facilities: Parking, toilets, shop, full disabled access and adapted toilets

Halifax

DUKE OF WELLINGTON'S REGIMENT
(WEST RIDING) MUSEUM

1 mile from town centre on the A647 to Queensbury and Bradford

The Duke of Wellington's Regiment (West Riding) Museum, Bankfield Museum, Boothtown Road, Halifax,
West Yorkshire HX3 6HG
T: 01422 354823 F: 01422 349020
E: rhq@dukesrhq.demon.co.uk

Curatorial Adviser: Mr John Spencer

Duke of Wellington's (West Riding) Regiment, 33rd Duke of Wellington's Regiment, 33rd (or 1st Yorkshire West Riding) Regiment of Foot, 33rd Regiment of Foot, Earl of Huntingdon's Regiment of Foot, 76th Regiment of Foot, 76th (Hindoostan) Regiment of Foot

The Collection illustrates the history of the Regiment from the raising of the 33rd Foot in 1702 and the 76th Foot in 1787 to the present day. The Museum has undergone a recent redesign to tell the story of the Regiment through the eyes of the soldiers who served in it. Each period case focuses on two or three soldiers and tells their story in their own words through recordings and displays of their life in the Regiment. Other exhibits relate to the local Volunteer, Militia and Territorial Forces and there are displays of objects associated with the Iron Duke himself and the Regiment's heritage as a name synonymous with rugby in the British Army. Access to the Regimental archive is by appointment.

Opening Hours: Tue–Sat and bank holiday Mondays 10am–5pm, Sun 1pm–4pm

Admission: Free

Facilities: Parking, toilets, shop, lecture room, disabled access

YORKSHIRE

For a detailed map, go to **www.streetmap.co.uk** and type in the post code of the museum

Hull

4TH BATTALION EAST YORKSHIRE REGIMENT COLLECTION

 4th Bn East Yorkshire Regiment Collection, Ferens Art Gallery, Queen Victoria Square, Kingston-upon-Hull HU1 3RA
T: 01482 613923 F: 01482 613710

Curator: Vanessa Salter
(Keeper of Social History)

The Collection, which also includes items from the East Yorks Militia and Rifle Volunteers, is temporarily in store but may be viewed by appointment.

Richmond

GREEN HOWARDS REGIMENTAL MUSEUM

Town centre location

Green Howards Regimental Museum, Trinity Church Square, Richmond, North Yorkshire DL10 4QN
T and F: 01748 822133
E: greenhowardsmus@aol.com
www.greenhowards.org.uk

Curator: Mr David Tetlow MA, AMA

Green Howards (Alexandra, Princess of Wales's Own Yorkshire Regiment), Alexandra Princess of Wales's Own Regiment of Yorkshire, Princess of Wales's Own (Yorkshire Regiment), 19th (1st Yorkshire North Riding) Regiment of Foot, 19th Regiment of Foot, Beauclerk's Regiment, Howard's Regiment, Sutton's Regiment, Erle's Regiment, Colonel Luttrell's Companies of Foot, North Riding Rifle Volunteer Corps, Princess of Wales's Own Yorkshire Regiment Territorial Battalions, Princess of Wales's Own Yorkshire Regiment Volunteer Battalions, North Yorkshire Regiment of Militia, North Yorkshire Light Infantry Regiment of Militia, North Yorkshire Rifles (Militia), Princess of Wales's Own (Yorkshire Regiment) Militia

An excellent collection of well-presented items on four floors illustrating the 300-year history of this famous Regiment and its close links with the North Riding of Yorkshire. Rich displays of uniforms, badges, headdresses and silver are complemented by an extensive medal collection with an interactive computer guide. There are special cases dedicated to the Ladies of the Regiment, and the Richmond Drummer Boy legend. Highlights of the Collection include Napoleon's snuff box, Oliver Cromwell's family bible, soldiers' uniforms from the Crimean War and uniforms and headdress from 1786 to 2006. Access to the Regimental archive is available by appointment.

Opening Hours: Oct 2006–Mar 2007 closed for refurbishment.
Apr–mid May: Mon–Sat 9.30am–4.30pm. Easter Sunday

2pm–4.30pm. Mid May–Sep: Mon–Sat 9.30am–4.30pm, Sun 2pm–4.30pm.

Admission: Adults £3.50, seniors £3, children £2.50

Facilities: Resource centre, shop, disabled access

Rotherham

YORK AND LANCASTER REGIMENT MUSEUM

Short walk from both bus and railway stations. By car access from M1(north) at J35 and then A629 to Rotherham, from M1 (south) at J33 then A63, from A1 take A630

 York and Lancaster Regiment Museum, Central Library and Arts Centre, Walker Place, Rotherham, South Yorkshire S65 1JH
T: 01709 336624 F: 01709 336628
E: karl.noble@rotherham.gov.uk
www.rotherham.gov.uk

Curator: Karl Noble

York and Lancaster Regiment, 65th (2nd Yorkshire North Riding) Regiment of Foot, 65th Regiment of Foot, 84th (York and Lancaster) Regiment of Foot, 84th Regiment of Foot, 84th Royal Highland Emigrant Corps, Eyre Coote's 84th Regiment of Foot

A comprehensive collection of uniforms, weapons, equipment and campaign relics traces the history of the Yorks and Lancs and its forebears the 65th and 84th Regiments of Foot from 1758 to 1968 through a chronological series of displays. Specific cases are dedicated to the Militia, Volunteers and Territorials, the Band, Silver and Sport. There is also a medals display which includes nine Victoria Crosses.

Opening Hours: Mon–Sat 9.30am–5pm. Closed Sun and bank holidays.
NB: appointments must be made to speak to the Curator.

Admission: Free

Facilities: Refreshments, toilets, shop, disabled access, adjacent parking

YORKSHIRE

York

KOHIMA MUSEUM 7

South of city centre, on A19 Fulford Road

Kohima Museum, Imphal Barracks, Fulford Road, York YO10 4AU
T: 01904 665806 / 635212
E: thekohimamuseum@hotmail.com

2nd

Curator: Major Nigel Magrane

Kohima Garrison (1944), 2nd Infantry Division and 33 Indian Brigade (1944)

The collection commemorates the Battle of Kohima and follows the fortunes of the 2nd Division up to and including its role in crossing the Irrawady. Almost all the objects have been donated by veterans and their relatives making it a very personal collection that sees the battle through the eyes of those who fought it.

Opening Hours: Thu 9am–12pm. Other days (less Sun) by appointment

Admission: Free

Facilities: Parking, toilets, shop, disabled access

PRINCE OF WALES'S OWN REGIMENT OF YORKSHIRE MUSEUM 8

Centre of York, opposite Clifford's Tower. Approximately a 15-minute walk from the station

Prince of Wales's Own Regiment of Yorkshire Museum, 3 Tower Street, York YO1 9SB
T: 01904 461010 F: 01904 658824
E: regsec@pwoyorkshire.army.mod.uk
www.army.mod.uk also
www.yorkshireregiment.mod.uk

Curator: Major N Allbeury MBE

Prince of Wales's Own Regiment of Yorkshire, West Yorkshire Regiment (The Prince of Wales's Own), Prince of Wales's Own (West Yorkshire Regiment), 14th (Buckinghamshire) (Prince of Wales's Own) Regiment of Foot, 14th (or the Buckinghamshire) Regiment of Foot, 14th (or the Bedfordshire) Regiment of Foot, 14th Regiment of Foot, Sir Edward Hales's Regiment of Foot, East Yorkshire Regiment (Duke of York's Own), East Yorkshire Regiment, 15th (or the Yorkshire East Riding) Regiment of Foot, 15th Regiment of Foot, Sir William Clifton's Regiment of Foot

The collection covers the history of two famous Yorkshire Regiments, both raised in 1685 by King James II. Displays of uniforms, badges, medals, silver, weapons, trophies, pictures and photographs illustrate the lives and service of both Regiments over a period of 300 years. Objects related to the successor Regiment, The Prince of Wales's Own Yorkshire Regiment, continue the story from 1958 and the most recent, 2006, amalgamation into The Yorkshire Regiment is also covered. The archives of the West Yorkshire Regiment and East Yorkshire Regiment are also available, by appointment, for research of family history by relatives of soldiers who served in the Regiments.

The museum is located in the same building as that of the Royal Dragoon Guards.

Opening Hours: Mon–Sat 9.30am–4.30pm. Closed Christmas and New Year

Admission: Adults £2, seniors/children £1, groups/school parties by appointment

Facilities: Toilets, shop, disabled access. Public Car Park 100m (opposite Hilton Hotel)

QUEEN'S OWN YORKSHIRE YEOMANRY 9

South of city centre, on A19 Fulford Road

The Queen's Own Yorkshire Yeomanry Museum, Yeomanry Barracks, Fulford Road, York YO10 4ES
T: 01482 881974 F: 01482 881974
E: Dominic.Peacock@hullcc.gov.uk

Curator: Dominic Peacock

The Queen's Own Yorkshire Yeomanry, The Yorkshire Hussars, The Queen's Own Yorkshire Dragoons, the East Riding Yeomanry

A small collection of artefacts and memorabilia from Yorkshire's Yeomanry Regiments. The Museum can be visited by prior appointment with the Yorkshire Squadron Office of the Queen's Own Yeomanry which can be contacted on 01904 620320. For information on the collections and regimental records and to contact the Old Comrades Association please contact the Regimental Secretary, Dominic Peacock, on the telephone number and email address shown above.

For a detailed map, go to **www.streetmap.co.uk** and type in the post code of the museum

ROYAL DRAGOON GUARDS

Centre of York, opposite Clifford's Tower. Approximately a 15-minute walk from the station

Royal Dragoon Guards Museum,
3 Tower Street, York YO1 9SB
T: 01904 642036 F: 01904 642036
E: hhq@rdgmuseum.org.uk
www.rdgmuseum.org.uk

Curator: Captain WA Hensall

Dragoon Guards (Princess Royal's), 7th (Princess Royal's) Dragoon Guards, 5th Royal Inniskilling Dragoons Guards, 5th Inniskilling Dragoon Guards, 5th/6th Dragoons, 5th Dragoon Guards (Princess Charlotte of Wales's), 5th (Princess Charlotte of Wales's) Dragoon Guards, 5th Dragoon Guards, Inniskilling (6th Dragoons), 6th (Inniskilling) Dragoons, 6th (Enniskilling) Regiment of Dragoons, 6th or Inniskilling Regiment of Dragoons, 6th (Inniskilling) Regiment of Dragoons

The museum tells the story of the 4th/7th Royal Dragoon Guards from 1685, when six Troops of Horse were raised for service under King James II, and continues up to the Regiment's amalgamation with the 5th Royal Inniskilling Dragoon Guards to form the present Royal Dragoons Guards. It includes artefacts from all the antecedent regiments dating back to their formation in the 1680s. The regimental archive is held in the same building and may be viewed by appointment.

Opening Hours: Mon–Sat 9.30am–4.30pm. Closed Christmas and New Year

Admission: Adults £2, seniors/children £1, groups/school parties by appointment

Facilities: Toilets, shop, disabled access. Public Car Park 100m (opposite Hilton Hotel)

YORKSHIRE

North East

2

1

Newcastle
upon Tyne
4 5

Carlisle

3

1	Alnwick:	**Royal Regiment of Fusiliers**
2	Berwick-upon-Tweed:	**King's Own Scottish Borderers**
3	Durham:	**Durham Light Infantry**
4	Gateshead:	**101 (Northumbrian) Regiment RA(V)**
5	Newcastle upon Tyne:	**The Light Dragoons (15th/19th King's Royal Hussars) and Northumberland Hussars**

Alnwick

THE FUSILIERS MUSEUM OF NORTHUMBERLAND

Along old A1, or bus to town Market Place, then a short walk

The Fusiliers Museum of Northumberland
The Abbott's Tower, Alnwick Castle,
Alnwick, Northumberland NE66 1NG
T: 01665 602152 F: 01665 605257
E:fusnorthld@aol.com
www.northumberlandfusiliers.org.uk

Curator: Captain Tony Adamson

Royal Regiment of Fusiliers, Royal Northumberland Fusiliers, Northumberland Fusiliers, 5th Regiment of Foot (Northumberland Fusiliers), 5th (or the Northumberland) Regiment of Foot, 5th Regiment of Foot, Lord O'Brien's Regiment (or the Irish Regiment)

The museum covers the history of the Royal Northumberland Fusiliers from its raising in 1674 up to and including its more recent post-1968 history as part of the Royal Regiment of Fusiliers. Housed on three floors of a tower in historic Alnwick Castle, the collection tells the story of this famous Regiment by reference to the lives of its soldiers, their families and the communities from which they came. The regimental archive and library may be viewed by appointment.

Opening Hours: Easter–Oct: daily 11am–5pm

Admission: Free after payment for entry to the Castle

Facilities: Shop, archives (by appointment, giving at least two weeks notice)

Berwick-upon-Tweed

KING'S OWN SCOTTISH BORDERERS MUSEUM

On the Parade, near the town centre off Church Street

King's Own Scottish Borderers Regimental Museum, The Barracks, Berwick-upon-Tweed, Northumberland, TD15 1DG
T: 01289 307426
F: 01289 331928
E: info@kosb.co.uk
www.kosb.co.uk/museum.htm

Curator: Lt Col CGO Hogg OBE, DL

King's Own Scottish Borderers, King's Own Borderers, 25th (or King's Own Borderers) Regiment of Foot, 25th (or the Sussex) Regiment of Foot, 25th (Edinburgh) Regiment of Foot, Earl of Leven's Regiment of Foot (The Edinburgh Regiment)

The museum covers the history of the Regiment from 1689 to the present day with displays of uniforms, badges, medals, weapons and relics from the various campaigns in which it has been involved. Tableaux and dioramas dramatically bring to life the Regiment's battles and aspects of the soldier's profession.

Opening Hours: 1 Apr–30 Sep: Mon–Sat 10am–5pm, closed Sun 1 Oct–31 Mar: Mon–Sat 10am–4pm, closed Sun

Admission: Adults £3.30, concessions £2.50, children age 5–16 £1.70. Free admission for members of English Heritage and serving members of the Armed Forces. Reduced price for members of Historic Scotland and CADW. Charges will increase during 2007.

Facilities: Toilets, shop, refreshments. Public car park nearby

Durham

DURHAM LIGHT INFANTRY MUSEUM

Approximately 50 yards from station, half a mile north of city centre off A691

 The DLI Museum and Durham Art Gallery,
Aykley Heads, Durham City DH1 5TU
T: 0191 3842214
F: 0191 3861770
E: dli@durham.gov.uk
www.durham.gov.uk/dli

Curator: Mr Stephen Shannon

Durham Light Infantry, (Durham) Light Infantry, 68th (or the Durham) Regiment of Foot, 68th Regiment of Foot, 106th Bombay Light Infantry, 2nd European Regiment Bombay Light Infantry (Honourable East India Company), 2nd Bombay European Regiment of Foot (Honourable East India Company), Durham Militia, Rifle Volunteers and Home Guard

The museum tells the story of the Regiments from its raising in 1758 to its absorption into the Light Infantry in 1968, with particular emphasis on the two world wars. The displays focus on the experience of war using letter and diary extracts, plus the recorded voices of DLI soldiers, to describe the life of the Regiment in the context of the Durham community from which it was drawn. The regimental archive is in the Durham County Record Office (T: 0191 3833253), a short walk from the museum. The catalogue, including all photographs, is available online on the Record Office website.

Opening Hours: 1 Apr–31 Oct: 10am–5pm
1 Nov–31 Mar: 10am–4pm. Closed Christmas Day

Admission: Adults £3, concessions £2, children £1.25, family ticket £7. Special rates for groups and school parties

Facilities: Parking, refreshments, toilets, lecture room, shop, disabled access, picnic area, corporate events

Gateshead

101 (NORTHUMBRIAN) REGIMENT ROYAL ARTILLERY (VOLUNTEERS) MUSEUM　4

1.5 miles south of the River Tyne, to the west of the A167

 101 (Northumbrian) Regt RA(V) Museum,
Napier Armoury, Alexandra Road,
Tyne and Wear NE8 4HX
T: 0191 239 6130 F: 0191 239 6132

Curator: Major C Whitley

A small collection covering the history of the Regiment.

Opening Hours: By appointment only

Admission: Free

Facilities: Parking, toilets, lecture room

Newcastle upon Tyne

THE LIGHT DRAGOONS (15TH/19TH KING'S ROYAL HUSSARS)　5

and

NORTHUMBERLAND HUSSARS MUSEUM COLLECTIONS

A short walk from Newcastle Central Station

Discovery Museum, Blandford Square,
Newcastle upon Tyne NE1 4JA
T: 0191 232 6789 F: 0191 230 2614
E: roberta.twinn@twmuseums.org.uk
www.twmuseums.org.uk or mail @lightdragoons.org.uk

Curator: Mr Alec Coles and
Captain PE Kingham

The Light Dragoons, 15th/19th King's Royal Hussars, 15th King's Hussars, 15th (King's) Light Dragoons, 1st (King's Royal) Light Dragoons, 15th Light Dragoons (Eliott's Light Horse), 19th Royal Hussars (Queen Alexandra's Own), 19th (Prince of Wales's Own) Hussars, 19th Hussars Bengal European Light Cavalry (Honourable East India Company), 19th Light Dragoons (Drogheda's Horse), Northumberland Hussars, Northumberland and Newcastle Volunteer Cavalry Imperial Yeomanry (1900-1902), 108th (NH) Anti-Tank Regiment RA, 274th (NH) Light Anti-Aircraft Battery RA Queen's Own Yeomanry

The regimental collections are on display in the Soldier's Life Gallery of the Discovery Museum and that theme characterises the displays which reflect the various stages of a soldier's life in a cavalry regiment. These include recruitment, training, life in war and peace, death or retirement. The objects on display include uniforms, badges and regimental memorabilia. There is extensive use of realistic mannequins and evocative scene setting as well as a short film of life in The Light Dragoons. The Gallery has recently undergone major refurbishment and houses an excellent, well-presented collection.

Opening Hours: Mon–Sat 10am–5pm, Sun 2–5pm

Admission: Free

Facilities: Parking, refreshments, toilets, shop, disabled access, corporate events

NORTH EAST

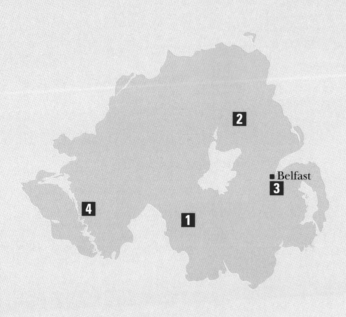

1	Armagh:	**Royal Irish Fusiliers**
2	Ballymena:	**Royal Irish Regiment**
3	Belfast:	**Royal Ulster Rifles**
4	Enniskillen:	**Royal Inniskilling Fusiliers**

N. IRELAND

Armagh

ROYAL IRISH FUSILIERS MUSEUM ▮1

Sovereign's House can be found at one end of The Mall about 20 metres from the Court House and a 5-minute walk from the Translink Bus station

Royal Irish Fusiliers Regimental Museum, Sovereign's House, The Mall, Armagh, Co. Armagh BT61 9DL
T: 0283 752 2911 F: 0283 752 2911
E: Rylirfusiliermus@aol.com
www.rirfus-museum.freeserve.co.uk

Curator: Ms Amanda Moreno MA

Royal Irish Regiment, Royal Irish Rangers, Royal Irish Fusiliers (Princess Victoria's), Princess Victoria's (Royal Irish Fusiliers), 87th (or Royal Irish Fusiliers) Regiment of Foot, 87th (Prince of Wales's Own Irish Fusiliers) Regiment of Foot, 87th (or Prince of Wales's Own Irish) Regiment of Foot, 87th (or Prince of Wales's Irish) Regiment of Foot, 89th (Princess Victoria's) Regiment of Foot, 89th Regiment of Foot, Armagh, Cavan and Monaghan Militias

The museum is housed in the recently refurbished Sovereign's House. The Eagle Takers Gallery won the Best Exhibition in Ireland award in 2003. The collection contains the uniforms, medals, regalia and the two Victoria Crosses won by the Regiment. The regimental archive and library may be viewed by appointment.

Opening Hours: Mon–Fri 10am–12.30pm and 1.30–4pm. Closed Christmas Day and New Year's Day

Admission: Free

Facilities: Toilets, lecture room, shop

Ballymena

ROYAL IRISH REGIMENT MUSEUM ▮2

East of town centre and north of swimming pool

Royal Irish Regiment Museum, St Patrick's Barracks, Ballymena, Co. Antrim BT43 7BH
T: 028 2566 1386 F: 028 2566 1378
E: hqrirish@royalirishregiment.co.uk
www.royalirishregiment.co.uk

Curator: Captain Mark Hagan

The Royal Irish Regiment (27th (INNISKILLING) 83rd, 87th and The Ulster Defence Regiment), Royal Irish Rangers (27th, 83rd, 86th, 87th, 89th and 108th Foot), Ulster Defence Regiment

The museum traces the history of the Regiment from the raising of its most senior antecedent, the Royal Inniskilling Fusiliers in 1689 to the present day, with an emphasis on the activities of the Royal Irish Regiment and its immediate predecessors the Royal Irish Rangers and the Ulster Defence Regiment.

Opening Hours: Wed and Sat 1pm–5pm or by appointment

Admission: Adults £2, seniors and children £1

Facilities: Parking, toilets, shop, disabled access

Belfast

ROYAL ULSTER RIFLES MUSEUM ▮3

Close to the city centre in the cathedral quarter

Royal Ulster Rifles Museum, 5 Waring Street Belfast BT1 2EW
T: 028 9023 2086 F: 028 9023 2086
E: rurmuseum@yahoo.co.uk

Curator: Captain J Knox

Royal Irish Regiment, Royal Irish Rangers, Royal Ulster Rifles, Royal Irish Rifles, 83rd (County of Dublin) Regiment of Foot, 83rd Regiment of Foot (Fitch's Grenadiers), 86th (Royal County Down) Regiment of Foot, 86th Regiment of Foot (Cuyler's Shropshire Volunteers)

The museum houses an extensive collection of uniforms, badges, medals and regimental memorabilia covering the history of the Regiment and the campaigns in which it has fought since its formation in 1793. The collection is well supported by digitised records and books.

Opening Hours: Mon–Fri 10am–12.30pm and 2pm–4pm (3pm on Fri). Appointments preferred

Admission: Adults £1. Free to serving and former members of the Regiment, seniors and children

Facilities: Shop, limited disabled access

N. IRELAND

Enniskillen

ROYAL INNISKILLING FUSILIERS MUSEUM 5

P 🧍 🧍 📷 🎧

South of town centre overlooking the River Erne. Well signposted

Royal Inniskilling Fusiliers Museum
The Castle, Enniskillen,
Co Fermanagh BT74 7HL
T: 028 6632 3142 F: 028 6632 0359
E: museum@inniskilling.com
www.inniskilling.com

Curator: Major JM Dunlop

Royal Irish Regiment, Royal Inniskilling Fusiliers, 27th (Inniskilling) Regiment of Foot, Colonel Zachariah Tiffin's Enniskillen Regiment of Foot, 108th (Madras Infantry) Regiment of Foot, 3rd (Madras) European Regiment (Honourable East India Company)

An important regimental collection tracing the history of Ireland's senior infantry regiment from its formation in 1689 to its amalgamation in 1968. It features a wide range of uniforms, weapons, silver, medals, vehicles and regimental memorabilia including eight Victoria Crosses awarded during World War I and the bugle that sounded the advance of the 36th (Ulster) Division at the Battle of the Somme. The collection is displayed in chronological order in the Keep of Enniskillen Castle. The regimental library and archive may be viewed by appointment with the curator.

Opening Times: May, Jun and Sep: Mon and Sat 2pm–5pm, Tue–Fri 10am–5pm. Jul and Aug: Mon, Sat and Sun 2pm–5pm. Oct–Apr: Mon 2pm–5pm, Tue–Fri 10am–5pm. Open bank holidays 10am–5pm

Admission: Adults £2.75, children £1.65, senior citizens £2.20, students £2.20, family rate £7.15 (2 adults + 3 children). Concession rates for groups

Facilities: Parking, toilets, shop, AV virtual tour for visitors with a disability

N. IRELAND

Scotland

1	Aberdeen:	**Gordon Highlanders**
2	Ayr:	**Ayrshire Yeomanry**
3	Cupar:	**Fife and Forfar Yeomanry**
4	Edinburgh:	**Royal Scots Dragoon Guards**
5	Edinburgh:	**Royal Scots**
6	Fort George:	**Queen's Own Highlanders**
7	Glasgow:	**Royal Highland Fusiliers**
8	Hamilton:	**Cameronians (Scottish Rifles)**
9	Perth:	**Black Watch**
10	Stirling:	**Argyll and Sutherland Highlanders**

SCOTLAND

Aberdeen

THE GORDON HIGHLANDERS MUSEUM

2.5 miles west of the city. No 14 or 15 bus from Union Street to Queen's Road/Viewfield Road

 The Gordon Highlanders Museum, St Luke's, Viewfield Road, Aberdeen AB15 7XH
T: 01224 311200 F: 01224 319323
E: museum@gordonhighlanders.com
www.gordonhighlanders.com

Curator: Sarah Malone

The Highlanders (Seaforth, Gordons and Camerons), Gordon Highlanders, 75th (Stirlingshire) Regiment of Foot, 75th Regiment of Foot, 75th (Highland) Regiment of Foot (Abercromby's Highlanders), 92nd (Gordon Highlanders) Regiment of Foot, 92nd (Highland) Regiment of Foot, 100th (Gordon Highlanders) Regiment of Foot, The London Scottish (Gordon Highlanders)

The museum, which is a Visit Scotland 5-star credited museum, houses an important collection of uniforms, badges, medals and regimental memorabilia illustrating the history of this famous Highland Regiment from the Napoleonic Wars through to recent operations in support of the United Nations. The exhibitions include interactive displays, sound stations, films, and models illustrating the deeds for which this Regiment is renowned. The full regimental archive is kept on site and access is available by appointment with the curator. There is also a programme of educational and recreation events and activities for all ages.

Opening Hours: First Tue in Apr–last Sun in Oct: Tue–Sat 10.30am–4.30pm, Sun 12.30pm–4.30pm, Mon Closed. Nov–Mar: open by appointment only

Admission: Adults £3.50, seniors £2.50, children £1.50, family ticket £8.50

Facilities: Parking, tea-room, toilets, shop, garden, disabled access, corporate events and meetings

Ayr

AYRSHIRE YEOMANRY MUSEUM

 Ayrshire Yeomanry Museum, Rozelle House Galleries, Monument Road, Ayr KA7 4NQ
T: 01292 445447 F: 01292 442065
E: gah@btinternet.com

Curator: George Hay (Tel: 01292 264091)

Ayrshire (Earl of Carrick's Own) Yeomanry

The museum collection traces the history of the Regiment from its formation in 1793, through its service as cavalry in South Africa, infantry in World War I and artillery in World War II. The displays include uniformed figures, medals, weapons, maps, photographs, paintings and memorabilia from the Regiment's various campaigns. The Regiment is now part of the Queen's Own Yeomanry.

Opening Hours: Apr–Oct only: Mon–Sat 10am–5pm, Sun 2–5pm

Admission: Free

Facilities: Parking, refreshments, toilets, shop, disabled access, corporate events

Cupar

FIFE AND FORFAR YEOMANRY COLLECTION

 Fife and Forfar Yeomanry Collection, Yeomanry House, Castlebank Road, Cupar, Fife HY15 4BL
T: 01334 656155 F: 01334 652345

Curator: Captain Preece

A small regimental collection, library and archive to which admission is by appointment only.

Facilities: Parking, toilets, lecture room

Edinburgh

THE ROYAL SCOTS DRAGOON GUARDS MUSEUM

Located within Edinburgh Castle

The Royal Scots Dragoon Guards Museum, The Castle, Edinburgh EH1 2YT
T: 0131 310 5100 F: 0131 310 5101
E: homehq@scotsdg.org.uk

Regimental Secretary: Lieutenant Colonel RJ Binks

The Royal Scots Dragoon Guards (Carabiniers and Greys) 1971 from Royal Scots Greys (2nd Dragoons) and 3rd Carabiniers (Prince of Wales's Dragoon Guards).

Antecedent Regiments:3rd Carabiniers, 1928 from 3rd/6th Dragoon Guards, 1922 3rd Dragoon Guards (Prince of Wales's), previously 3rd (Prince of Wales's) Dragoon Guards, 3rd Regiment of Dragoon Guards and 4th Regiment of Horse, 1922 The Carabiniers (6th Dragoon Guards), previously 6th Dragoon Guards (The Carabiniers), 3rd Irish Horse, 7th Horse, King's Carabiniers, 8th Horse, 9th Regiment of Horse, Royal Scots Greys previously

SCOTLAND

All information is correct at the time of going to press, but **you are advised to contact museums before making a visit**

69

named Royal North British Dragoons, Royal Regiment of Scots Dragoons

An important collection illustrating the history of Scotland's only cavalry regiment and its English and Scottish antecedents dating back to 1678. Famous episodes in regimental history, such as the charge of the Royal Scots Greys at the Battle of Waterloo in 1815, the same Regiment's action in the 1943 Italian campaign and the 3rd Carabiniers epic assault in Burma are given pride of place amongst well presented displays of uniformed figures, paintings, photographs and regimental trophies from its various campaigns. Interactive displays and exhibits take the visitor right up to the Regiment's most recent involvement in Iraq. The regimental archive and library may be viewed by appointment with the Regimental Secretary.

Opening Hours: Daily 9.30am–5.30pm (4.30pm in Winter: Oct–Mar)

Admission: Free after payment of Castle entry charge

Facilities: Shop (0131 220 4387), refreshments and toilets within Edinburgh Castle. Limited parking

ROYAL SCOTS REGIMENTAL MUSEUM

Located within Edinburgh Castle

Royal Scots Regimental Museum,
The Castle, Edinburgh EH1 2YT
T: 0131 310 5016 F: 0131 310 5019
E: rhqrs@btconnect.com
www.theroyalscots.co.uk

Curator: Lieutenant Colonel RP Mason

Royal Scots (The Royal Regiment), Royal Scots (The Lothian Regiment), Lothian Regiment (Royal Scots), 1st or The Royal Scots Regiment, Royal Regiment of Foot, 1st Regiment of Foot or Royal Scots, 1st or Royal Regiment of Foot, Royal Regiment of Foot, Earl of Dumbarton's Regiment (1st Foot), Le Regiment de Douglas, Le Regiment d'Hebron

This Regiment, raised for King Charles 1st by Sir John Hepburn in 1633, is the oldest in the British Army. The museum illustrates its history chronologically through displays of paintings, artefacts, uniforms, silver, badges and medals. The regimental archive and library are on site and may be viewed by appointment.

Opening Hours: Apr–Sep: daily 9.30am–5.30pm. Oct–Mar: Mon–Fri 9.30am–4pm. Closed Christmas and New Year

Admission: Free after payment of Castle entry charge

Facilities: Parking, refreshments, toilets, shop

SCOTLAND

Fort George

THE HIGHLANDERS REGIMENTAL MUSEUM

15 miles east of Inverness

The Highlanders Regimental Museum,
Fort George, Ardersier,
Inverness-shire IV2 2TD
T: 0131 310 8701
E: RegtmuseumQOHldr@aol.co

Curator: Mr Kelvin Hunter

The Highlanders (Seaforth, Gordons, Camerons),Queen's Own Highlanders (Ross-shire Buffs, The Duke of Albany's), 72nd (or The Duke of Albany's Own Highlanders) Regiment of Foot, 72nd Regiment of Foot, 72nd (Highland) Regiment of Foot, 78th (Highland) Regiment of Foot (or the Ross-shire Buffs), 78th Regiment of (Highland) Foot, Queen's Own Cameron Highlanders, 79th Queen's Own Cameron Highlanders, 79th Regiment of Foot (or Cameron Highlanders), 79th Regiment of Foot (or Cameronian Highlanders), 79th Regiment of Foot (or Cameronian Volunteers), Lovat Scouts, Liverpool Scottish, 51st Highland Volunteers

The Regimental Museum Collection of the Queen's Own Highlanders is the private collection of a regiment with over 200 years association with Fort George. The Museum comprises a unique collection of medals, uniforms and accoutrements, weapons, paintings and prints, colours and pipe banners, mess plate, ceramics, and other artefacts covering the history of the Regiment back to 1778. The Museum also has a comprehensive library and archive collection to which researchers are welcome, and this includes original sources and published material on Fort George.

Opening Hours: Apr–Sep: daily 10am–6pm. Oct–Mar: Mon–Fri 10am–4pm. Closed Christmas and New Year

Admission: Free after payment of Fort George entry charge

Facilities: Parking, refreshments, toilets, lecture room, shop, disabled access

Glasgow

ROYAL HIGHLAND FUSILIERS MUSEUM

75 yards east of Charing Cross, bus to Charing Cross from Central Station

Royal Highland Fusiliers Museum, 518 Sauchiehall Street, Glasgow G2 3LW
T: 0141 332 5639 F: 0141 353 1493
E: assregsec@rhf.org.uk
www.rhf.org.uk

Curator: Colonel RL Steele TD DL

Royal Highland Fusiliers (Princess Margaret's Own Glasgow and Ayrshire Regiment), Royal Scots Fusiliers, 21st (Royal Scots Fusiliers) Regiment of Foot, 21st Regiment of Foot (or Royal North British Fuzileers), Royal Regiment of North British Fuzileers, North British Fuzileers, The Earl of Mar's Regiment of Foot, Highland Light Infantry (City of Glasgow Regiment), 71st (Highland Light Infantry), 71st (Highland) Regiment of Foot (Light Infantry), 71st (Glasgow Highland) Regiment of Foot (Light Infantry), 71st (Glasgow Highland) Regiment of Foot, 71st (Highland) Regiment of Foot, 73rd (Highland) Regiment of Foot – MacLeod's Highlanders, 74th (Highland) Regiment of Foot, 74th Regiment of Foot, 74th (Highland) Regiment of Foot – The Assaye Regiment, Glasgow Highlanders (9th Bn Highland Light Infantry)

The museum traces the history of the three regiments from which the Royal Highland Fusiliers are descended. Starting in 1678 the story carries through to the Regiment today. The collection is shown chronologically on two floors of interlinked galleries illustrating the many campaigns in which the Regiment has served with displays of weapons, uniforms, medals, music and regimental trophies and memorabilia. There is a good mix of artefacts, pictures, text and video screens. The regimental archive and library are held in the same building and may be viewed by appointment.

The building is of interest to those aware of Scottish design. The external façade and many of the interior details remain intact and reflect the style and influence of Charles Rennie Mackintosh.

Opening Hours: Mon–Fri 8.30am–4pm. Weekends and evenings by appointment

Admission: Free. Groups and school parties by appointment

Facilities: Toilets, lecture room, shop, disabled access

Hamilton

CAMERONIANS (SCOTTISH RIFLES) MUSEUM COLLECTION $\quad$ 8

Exit M74 at J6, right at first roundabout, across second, right at third to car park immediately on the left

Cameronians (Scottish Rifles) Museum Collection, Low Parks Museum, 129 Muir Street, Hamilton, South Lanarkshire ML3 6BJ
T: 01698 328232 F: 01698 328412
E: lowparksmuseum@southlanarkshire.gov.uk
www.southlanarkshire.gov.uk

Curator: Terry Mackenzie

Cameronians (Scottish Rifles), 26th (or Cameronian) Regiment of Foot, 26th Regiment of Foot, Earl of Angus's Regiment of Foot, 90th Light Infantry Regiment Perthshire Volunteers, 90th Regiment of Foot (or Perthshire Volunteers), 90th Perthshire Light Infantry, Lanarkshire Volunteers, Militia and Yeomanry Units

The Cameronians, formed in 1881 from the merger of the 26th and 90th Regiments of Foot, have a unique facet to their history, being the only regiment of the British Army to have a religious origin. Raised from Covenanters in 1698, the collection includes objects from the Covenanters period and from every major campaign in which the Regiment served until it disbanded in 1968, in preference to amalgamation, during a period of Army restructuring. Access to the archives (uncatalogued) is available by appointment.

Opening Hours: Mon–Sat 10am–5pm, Sun 12pm–5pm

Admission: Free

Facilities: Parking, toilets, lecture room, shop, disabled access, corporate events, civil weddings

Perth

BLACK WATCH REGIMENTAL MUSEUM $\quad$

Well signed and within easy walking distance of the city centre

Black Watch Regimental Museum, Balhousie Castle, Hay Street, Perth PH1 5HR
T: 0131 310 8530 F: 01738 643 245
E: rhq@theblackwatch.co.uk
www.theblackwatch.co.uk

Curator: Major RJW Proctor MBE

The Black Watch (Royal Highland Regiment), 42nd Royal Highland Regiment of Foot (The Black Watch), 42nd (The Royal Highland) Regiment of Foot, 42nd Regiment of Foot, Earl of Crawford's Regiment of Foot (The Highland Regiment), 73rd (Perthshire) Regiment of Foot, 73rd Regiment of Foot, 73rd (Highland) Regiment of Foot

The Collection covers the long history of the oldest of the Highland Regiments from its raising as six independent companies in 1725, until 2006 when it became a battalion of the Royal Regiment of Scotland. Displayed chronologically in seven rooms, each dedicated to a particular period in the Regiment's history, there are colours, uniforms, weapons, badges, medals, paintings and regimental trophies and artefacts illustrating some of the Regiment's many campaigns including the North American wars, the Napoleonic campaign, the Crimea, both world wars and more recent operations.

Opening Hours: May–Sep: Mon–Fri 10am–4.30pm. Oct–Apr: Mon–Fri 10am–3.30pm

Admission: Free

Facilities: Parking, toilets, shop

SCOTLAND

Stirling

ARGYLL AND SUTHERLAND HIGHLANDERS
REGIMENTAL MUSEUM

Located in Stirling Castle

Argyll and Sutherland Highlanders Regimental Museum,
The Castle, Stirling FK8 1EH
T: 01786 475165 F: 01786 446038
E: museum@argylls.co.uk
www.argylls.co.uk

Curator: Rod Mackenzie

Argyll and Sutherland Highlanders (Princess Louise's), Princess Louise's (Argyll and Sutherland Highlanders), 91st (Princess Louise's Argyllshire Highlanders) Regiment of Foot, 91st (Argyllshire Highlanders) Regiment of Foot, 91st (Argyllshire) Regiment of Foot, 91st Regiment of Foot, 91st (Argyllshire) Regiment of Foot (Highlanders), 98th (Argyllshire) Regiment of Foot (Highlanders), 93rd (Sutherland Highlanders) Regiment of Foot, 93rd (Highland) Regiment of Foot

This rich collection covers the history of the Regiment from its raising in Stirling in 1794. It occupies eight rooms and is divided into periodical sections which include the Crimea where the Regiment formed "The Thin Red Line", the Indian Mutiny, the Boer War, both world wars, Korea, Suez, Aden, Malaya and the Regiment's more recent operational deployments. Stories of military courage and gallantry are set in the human context of the Scottish communities from which the Regiment drew its soldiers and its strength. Objects on display include personal items, regimental colours, pipe banners, silver, trophies, medals and various items of period uniform and equipment, paintings and prints with an emphasis on associated eye-witness accounts, and related anecdotes. There are dioramas and a realistic model of a World War I trench. Access to the archives is available by appointment. Historical enquiries regarding the Regiment or museum can be sent to the postal or e-mail addresses above.

Opening Hours: Easter–Sep: Mon–Sat 9.30am–5pm.
Oct–Easter: Mon–Sat 10am–4.15pm

Admission: Free, after payment for Castle entry

Facilities: Parking, refreshments, toilets, shop

SCOTLAND

For a detailed map, go to **www.streetmap.co.uk** and type in the post code of the museum

Part II

Principal National Museums

Inverness

Glasgow · Edinburgh **10**

Newcastle upon Tyne

Carlisle

Belfast

York

13 · Leeds · Hull

Manchester

Liverpool **7** · Sheffield

Nottingham

11 · Norwich

Birmingham

Cambridge

6

Oxford

Cardiff · · LONDON

· Bristol **3 4 9**

5 8 12

2

Southampton

1 14

15 16

Plymouth

1	**Explosion! Museum of Naval Firepower**
2	**Fleet Air Arm Museum**
	Imperial War Museum
3	Imperial War Museum London
4	Churchill Museum and Cabinet War Rooms
5	HMS Belfast
6	Imperial War Museum Duxford
7	Imperial War Museum North
8	**National Army Museum**
9	**National Maritime Museum**
10	**National War Museum of Scotland**
	Royal Air Force Museum
11	Cosford
12	London
13	**Royal Armouries**
14	**Royal Marines Museum**
15	**Royal Naval Museum**
16	**Royal Navy Submarine Museum**

Gosport, Hampshire

EXPLOSION!

P 🚶 ♿ 📷 ♿ 🎖 ☕ 📖

Museum of Naval Firepower
Priddy's Hard, Gosport,
Hampshire PO12 4LE
T: 023 9250 5600
Email: info@explosion.org.uk
www.explosion.org.uk

Explosion! Museum of Naval Firepower, is a hands-on, interactive Museum set in the historic setting of a former gunpowder and munitions depot at Priddy's Hard, on the Gosport side of Portsmouth Harbour. Priddy's Hard was once a busy Naval Armament Supply Depot that provided the Royal Navy with its ammunition for over 200 years.

The museum houses a nationally important collection of guns and naval ordnance and illustrates the story of naval warfare from the days of gunpowder to modern missiles, from the days of the Battle of Trafalgar to the Gulf War. The two-hour tour of the museum includes a stunning multi-media film show set in the original 18th-century gunpowder vault, with the latest technology and interactive touch screens that bring the presentations to life.

There's a fascinating social history too, including the story of how 2,500 women worked on the site during its peak in World War II. It describes the role that Priddy's Hard played in naval operations worldwide for over 200 years, as well as its importance to the local Gosport community, which not only armed the Navy but also fed and watered it.

The galleries and displays which have been created represent a first phase of development for the Priddy's Hard site. It is intended that further phases will be developed using the buildings that currently house the extensive reserve collections opposite the Grand Magazine and the impressive 'E' magazine sited in the ramparts and reputedly constructed from no fewer than 3 million bricks.

Explosion! has a gift shop and waterside coffee shop area that are open to non-visitors, so please stop by and sample some of our traditional homemade lunches on the Camber Dock overlooking the stunning views of the harbour.

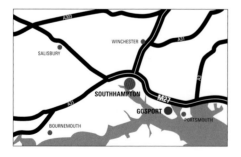

Opening Hours: Apr–Oct and every school holiday (except 24–26 Dec): Daily 10am–5.30pm
Nov–Mar: Thu, Sat and Sun 10am–4.30pm
Last admission: one hour before closing

Admission: Adult £5.50, senior £4.50, child £3.50, family ticket £15.00 (2+4) & Sun 10am–4.30pm

Directions for Travellers

By Road: M27 to junction 11. Follow A32 to Gosport and signs to Explosion! at Priddy's Hard

By Rail: Follow the mainline route to Portsmouth Harbour. Take the frequent ferry service across to Gosport (3 mins). From the ferry at Gosport, turn right and follow the Millennium Promenade to Explosion! at Priddy's Hard (20 mins walk) or a taxi to Forton Bridge (3 mins)

NATIONALS

Yeovilton, Somerset

FLEET AIR ARM MUSEUM

P 🚶 🚼 🍴 📷 ♿ 📕 📖 ☕

Royal Naval Air Station Yeovilton,
Somerset BA22 8HT
T: 01935 840565
F: 01935 842630
E: info@fleetairarm.com
www.fleetairarm.com

Director: Graham Mottram

The Fleet Air Arm Museum was originally opened by the Duke of Edinburgh on the 28th of May 1964 on the occasion of the 50th anniversary of the formation of the Royal Naval Air Service, the predecessor of the Fleet Air Arm. Over the ensuing 40 years the Museum has expanded from its modest beginnings when it housed just eight aircraft, to become Europe's largest naval aviation museum.

Occupying four enormous hangars and a climate-controlled storage hangar, the Museum has over 90 aircraft from the remains of the very first aircraft to have taken part in a naval battle (the Short 184 in 1916) to Harriers, a Phantom strike fighter and a Buccaneer complete with a nuclear bomb!

Visitors will experience what life's like on the busy flight deck of HMS Ark Royal. Arriving onto the flight deck from a simulated flight in a Wessex helicopter, visitors will find themselves among ten aircraft and at either end of the flight deck, enormous projection screens show a dramatic take off and landing sequence. Visitors feel they are really at sea!

In addition to the naval aircraft, the Fleet Air Arm Museum has the first British-built Concorde. Visitors can go on board and marvel at the 1960s technology, which made this amazing aircraft fly at more than twice the speed of sound.

The Museum is situated alongside RNAS Yeovilton, where, dependent upon operational demands visitors may see naval aircraft going through their rigorous training procedures.

There's a shop, restaurant and children's adventure play area. In fact, the Museum is so large, visitors need around four hours to begin to do it justice.

Opening Hours: Apr–Oct: Open daily 10am–5.30pm
Nov–Mar: Open Wed–Sun 10am–4.30pm. Closed 24–26 Dec

Admission: Serving personnel: £5. Ex-service personnel: £8.
Civilians: adults, £10, seniors £8, children £7, family (2+3) £30

Directions for Travellers:

The museum is located on the B3151 just off the A303 and A37. It is accessible from the M5 motorway, junction 25 at Taunton

Yeovilton is situated some seven miles north of Yeovil, 40 miles south of Bristol, 30 miles north of Weymouth and 30 miles southeast of Weston-Super-Mare

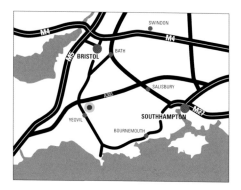

All information is correct at the time of going to press, but **you are advised to contact museums before making a visit**

NATIONALS

75

Imperial War Museum

WWW.IWM.ORG.UK

Director-General: Robert Crawford

The five branches of the Imperial War Museum explore the impact of conflict on people's lives in Britain and the Commonwealth since 1914 through unique historic buildings and fascinating exhibits, innovative, thought-provoking exhibitions and a wide variety of activities for all ages.

IMPERIAL WAR MUSEUM LONDON

The internationally acclaimed museum of 20th-century conflict

Lambeth Road, London SE1 6HZ
T: 020 7416 5320/5321

Opening hours: Daily 10am–6pm (closed 24–26 Dec)

Admission: Free

CHURCHILL MUSEUM AND CABINET WAR ROOMS

A museum dedicated to Churchill's life housed in his secret wartime headquarters

Clive Steps, King Charles Street, London SW1A 2AQ
T: 020 7930 6961

Opening hours: Daily 9.30am–6pm (closed 24–26 Dec)

Admission: £11 adults, £8.50 seniors and students; free to children under 16

HMS BELFAST

Europe's last big gun armoured warship of World War II

Morgan's Lane, Tooley Street, London SE1 2JH
T: 020 7940 6300

Opening hours: Daily Mar–Oct 10am–6pm. Nov–Feb 10am–5pm (closed 24–26 Dec)

£8.50 adults, £5.25 seniors and students, free to children under 16

IMPERIAL WAR MUSEUM DUXFORD

World-renowned aviation museum and heritage complex

Duxford
Cambridgeshire
CB2 4QR
T: 01223 835 000

Opening hours: Open daily from 10am (closed 24–26 Dec)

Admission: Charges apply to adults and seniors, free to children under 16 (Call 01223 835000 for more information)

IMPERIAL WAR MUSEUM NORTH

Iconic new museum illuminating how war shapes lives

The Quays, Trafford Wharf Rd, Trafford Park, Manchester M17 1TZ
T: 0161 836 4000

Opening hours: Daily Mar–Oct: 10am–6pm. Nov–Feb: 10am–5pm (closed 24–26 Dec)

Admission: Free

Directions for Travellers

Visit www.iwm.org.uk for directions to all five branches of the Imperial War Museum

NATIONALS

For a detailed map, go to **www.streetmap.co.uk** and type in the post code of the museum

Chelsea, London

NATIONAL ARMY MUSEUM

Royal Hospital Road, Chelsea,
London SW3 4HT
T: 020 7730 0717
F: 020 7823 6573
E: info@national-army-museum.ac.uk
www.national-army-museum.ac.uk

Director: Dr Alan Guy

In a chronological series of four major galleries the National Army Museum traces the history of the British Army and its role in the making of Britain from the middle ages to the present day. Its collection is a treasure trove of artefacts and archives that touch on events ranging from those of national and international importance, such as the American War of Independence or the end of British rule in India, to the conditions of life as a National Serviceman or an archer at Agincourt. Home to one of the largest collections of military costume in the world, the development of the British Army is well illustrated by mannequins in contemporary uniforms and equipment. The difficult and dangerous life of the British soldier and the changing world in which he has lived throughout the centuries is brought to life by interactive sound and visual displays. The collection also addresses wider themes such as the control and organization of the Army, the daily life of the soldier and civilian perceptions of the Army. The Museum's message, delivered through its displays and activities, is presented for a family audience.

The Templer Study Centre (open Thu–Fri 10am–5pm and on the 1st and 3rd Sat of each month) provides access to 80,000 books, a major collection (5 million items) of archives and prints and some 740,000 photographs. The Museum presents regular special exhibitions, events and lecture programmes, full details of which may be found on the website. The Museum's children's gallery – The Kids' Zone – provides learning and play opportunities that are suitable for ages 0–10.

Encompassing Militia, Yeomanry, Volunteers and the Territorial Army as well as the regular forces, the museum also looks at the armies of the British Empire and Commonwealth during the two world wars and tells the history of the Indian Army up to 1947. The collections of the pre-1922 Irish regiments of the British Army are dispersed amongst the collection as a whole. In addition the museum is home to the regimental collections of: The Buffs, 3rd Regiment of Foot, Royal East Kent Regiment, The Middlesex Regiment, 57th (or the West Middlesex) Regiment of Foot, 59th Regiment of Foot, 77th (The East Middlesex) Regiment of Foot (Duke of Cambridge's Own), 77th Regiment of Foot, Women's Royal Army Corps, Auxiliary Training Service, Women's Army Auxiliary Corps.

Opening Hours: Daily 10am–5.30pm. Closed 24–26 Dec, 1 Jan, Good Friday, early May bank holiday

Admission: Free

Facilities: Toilets, shop, e-commerce, restaurant, disabled access, library and research facilities, Society of Friends, hospitality packages, birthday parties

Directions for Travellers

Nearest Mainline railway station: Victoria

Nearest Underground station: Sloane Square

Buses: Nos 11, 19, 22 and 211 to King's Road
*   No 137 to Pimlico Road*
*   No 239 stops outside the Museum*

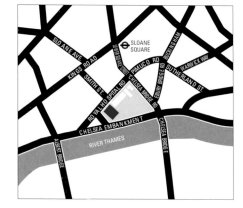

All information is correct at the time of going to press, but **you are advised to contact museums before making a visit**

77

Greenwich, London

NATIONAL MARITIME MUSEUM

MNATIONAL
ARITIME
MUSEUM

The Queen's House
and Royal Observatory, Greenwich

National Maritime Museum, Greenwich,
London SE10 9NF
T: 020 8858 4422 (8312 6565 recorded information)
F: 020 8312 6632
nmmweb@nmm.ac.uk
www.nmm.ac.uk

Director: Roy Clare

The national museum of seafaring, timekeeping and astronomy (est. 1934) occupies major buildings in the Maritime Greenwich World Heritage Site, between the Old Royal Naval College and Greenwich Royal Park. It includes the 17th-century Queen's House, designed by Inigo Jones, and the Royal Observatory, Greenwich, "home" of world time.

The NMM's pre-eminent maritime collections exceed 2.5 million items, many in themed displays covering topics including discovery, trade and empire, passengers by sea, the marine environment, Nelson and his navy, and interactive children's galleries. An "Atlantic world" gallery also opens in 2007, with one on the East to follow. The collections include major research holdings and have much of military interest, especially on national defence and the Royal Navy's historical role in the overseas projection of British imperial and economic power. However, it is much more than a naval museum and covers many other aspects of maritime social, scientific, technical and cultural history in very accessible ways (including an award-winning website). The Queen's House is the principal showcase for its world-class holdings of maritime art and a major British portrait collection: its navigational and astronomical instruments are primarily displayed at the Royal Observatory, where the "Time" galleries include John Harrison's famous chronometers, which solved the problem of finding longitude at sea. From spring 2007 the Observatory will also have a new 120-seat "live" planetarium and modern astronomy centre.

Opening Hours: Daily 10am–5pm (6pm in summer). Closed 25–26 Dec

Admission: Free (except some temporary exhibitions)

Facilities: Shops and cafés at main Museum and Observatory. Research library open Mon–Fri (Sat by appointment). Limited on-site parking. NMM parking at weekends only. See www.nmm.ac.uk for further details

Directions for travellers

Overground rail (Charing Cross, Cannon Street and Waterloo) or DLR to Cutty Sark for Maritime Greenwich

Note: There is restricted public car parking in Greenwich

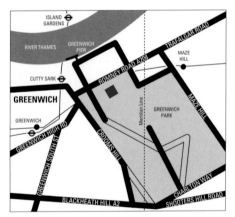

NATIONALS

For a detailed map, go to **www.streetmap.co.uk** and type in the post code of the museum

Edinburgh

NATIONAL WAR MUSEUM OF SCOTLAND

National War Museum of Scotland
Edinburgh Castle, Edinburgh EH1 2NG
T: 0131 247 4413
F: 0131 225 3848
E: info@nms.ac.uk
www.nms.ac.uk

Curator: Stuart Allan Senior Curator of Military History, National Museums of Scotland

War and military service have touched the lives of countless Scots, leaving their mark on Scotland's history, image and reputation abroad. Here, in the magnificent setting of Edinburgh Castle, explore over 400 years of the Scottish military experience.

Discover uniform, insignia and equipment, medals, decorations, weapons, paintings, ceramics and silverware, all of which throw light on Scotland's military history, from world-changing events to the everyday life of Scottish servicemen.

Six fascinating galleries evoke the power, drama and impact of war:

* **A Nation in Arms:** Find out about the influence of war, strategy and empire on the history of Scotland

* **A Grand Life for a Scotsman:** Explore military life, as experienced by the individual – from recruitment to retirement

* **Tools of the Trade:** See the weapons, equipment and clothing developed to meet the demands of war

* **Highland Soldier:** Uncover the story of a unique figure in military history, an icon of Scottish identity

* **In Defence:** Explore the military demands placed on the civilian population, in home defence and total war

* **Active Service:** Experience battle through the eyes of Scottish servicemen

The Museum library is open Tue and Fri 10am–1pm, and Wed and Thu 2–5pm

Opening Hours: Apr–Oct: Mon–Sun 9.45am–5.45pm. Nov–Mar: 9.45am–4.45pm

Admission: Included in admission to Edinburgh Castle.
Admission currently: adult £10.30, child £4.50, concessions £8.50 ; Last tickets sold at 5.15pm (4.15pm in winter).

Prices will increase in 2007

Directions for Travellers

Situated within Edinburgh Castle at the top of The Royal Mile, in the centre of Edinburgh, a few minutes' walk from Princes Street and Waverley station

NATIONALS

All information is correct at the time of going to press, but **you are advised to contact museums before making a visit**

79

Royal Air Force Museum

ROYAL AIR FORCE MUSEUM, COSFORD   **11**

🚶 👫 🖼 ♿ ☕

Cosford, Shifnal
Shropshire TF11 8UP
T: 01902 376 200
F: 01902 372 211
E: cosford@rafmuseum.org
www.rafmuseum.org

ROYAL AIR FORCE MUSEUM, LONDON   **12**

🚶 👫 ♿ ☕

Grahame Park Way,
London NW9 5LL
T: 020 8205 2266
F: 020 8200 1751
E: london@rafmuseum.org
www.rafmuseum.org

The Royal Air Force Museum is Britain's only national Museum dedicated wholly to aviation.

The Museum occupies two public sites at Hendon, London, and Cosford, Shropshire. Both tell the story of aviation with a unique brand of education and entertainment that make them a great free fun day out for all the family. Free parking and easy road and public transport ensure stress-free access to both.

Situated in the West Midlands, Cosford is acknowledged as one of the top public attractions in the area, and is unique in that it includes both indoor and outdoor aircraft exhibits. The Cosford Visitor Centre, which includes a restaurant and souvenir shop, makes a perfect take-off point for a tour of the Museum site – including the wartime hangars in which many of the aircraft are housed, a number of them the only remaining examples in the world. The display includes over 70 aircraft on view along with one of the finest collections of missiles, rockets and engines. Other features include the Michael Beetham Conservation Centre, the official British Airways Museum and a number of commercial passenger aircraft. Due to open in February 2007 is the National Cold War Exhibition.

The Museum at Hendon is situated in North West London, just a few tube stops from the centre of the capital. Amongst the 100-plus aircraft is the chance to see some great films, shows, artwork, medals and uniforms. The Battle of Britain Hall allows visitors to experience the dangerous days of 1940 when the country was under attack. With history sites and an awe-inspiring multimedia show, visitors can feel a part of the events that led up to World War II.

New to Hendon is the Milestones of Flight exhibition, a stunningly dramatic display including suspended aircraft, time-wall, touch-screen plinths and split-level viewing. On the other hand the beautifully restored Grahame White Factory is an example of an aircraft factory from the early days of British aviation. A historical building in its own right, it is now set to contain some classic aircraft of the time.

Opening Hours: daily 10am–6pm
Closed 24–26 Dec and 1 Jan

Admission: Free + free parking

Facilities: Toilets, refreshments,
disabled access, shop

Directions for Travellers

Cosford is on the A41, 1 mile south of junction 3 on the M54 and only 25 miles from Birmingham. It has own railway station and visitors can also fly in on weekdays by prior permission.

Directions for Travellers

Museum is signposted from the A1, M1, A41, A5 and A406. The local tube is Colindale (Northern Line) and it is also close to Mill Hill Broadway (Thameslink Rail). The 303 bus stops right outside.

For a detailed map, go to **www.streetmap.co.uk** and type in the post code of the museum

Leeds, Yorkshire

ROYAL ARMOURIES MUSEUM

Armouries Drive,
Leeds LS10 1LT
T: 0113 220 1916
E: enquiries@armouries.org.uk
www.royalarmouries.org

Museum Director: Peter Armstrong

The Royal Armouries is Britain's oldest national museum, and one of the oldest museums in the world.

It began life as the main royal and national arsenal housed in the Tower of London. Indeed the Royal Armouries has occupied buildings within the Tower for making and storing arms, armour and military equipment for as long as the Tower itself has been in existence.

As the museum's collections continued to expand the Tower became too small to house it all properly. In 1988 the Royal Armouries took a lease on Fort Nelson, a large 19th-century artillery fort near Portsmouth. This is now open to the public and displays the collection of artillery.

In 1996 the Royal Armouries moved the bulk of the collection of worldwide arms and armour to Leeds, thus allowing the Royal Armouries in the Tower to concentrate upon the display and interpretation of those parts of the collection which directly relate to the Tower of London. The new museum has been developed specifically to show the collections of the Royal Armouries in the best possible way.

The Royal Armouries Museum, Leeds has been built for the 21st century using the best of traditional museum design and it has been developed quite consciously to show its collections in relation to the real world in which we live. The displays seek to make the historical stories relevant by bringing them up to the present day. The building has, quite literally, been designed around the collections of the museum. The displays are intended to entertain and stimulate a desire to learn, and our intention has been to create a multi-layered experience to cater for the many different interests and interest levels of our visitors.

There are over 8,000 exhibits to see in our five themed galleries: War, Tournament, Oriental, Hunting and Self Defence. Costumed demonstrations, authentic re-enactments, entertaining films and interactive technology all give a true sense of history and throughout the year, live performances put you in the midst of the action. From April to October we recreate jousting tournaments in the tiltyard.

The Royal Armouries Museum spans 3,000 years of history – and is still relevant to the issues of power and conflict we live with today.

Opening Hours: Daily 10am–5pm (except 24 and 25 Dec).
The Tiltyard is open from Easter until the end of Oct for demonstrations of horse riding and falconry, weather permitting

Admission: Entry to the Museum is free but some activities and events may be chargeable

Facilities: Toilets, café, disabled access, library and research facilities

Directions for Travellers

By road: Exit M621 at J4. Follow brown signs for the Museum

Car parking: A 1,650-space, multi-storey car park is located 100m from the Museum and offers 24hr manned, CCTV monitored, secure parking

By bus or train: The Museum is a 20-minute walk from Leeds City centre and Leeds City railway station

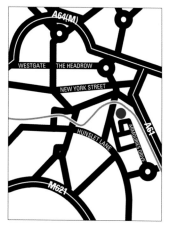

All information is correct at the time of going to press, but **you are advised to contact museums before making a visit**

NATIONALS

81

Southsea, Hampshire

ROYAL MARINES MUSEUM

The Royal Marines Museum
Southsea, Hampshire PO4 9PX
T: 023 9281 9385 F: 023 9283 8420
E: info@royalmarinesmuseum.co.uk
www.royalmarinesmuseum.co.uk

Director: Chris Newbery FMA
Curator: Ian Maine

The Royal Marines, Royal Marine Light Infantry, Royal Marine Artillery, Special Boat Service, Royal Marines Band Service

Housed in an imposing 19th-century building that once served as an Officers' Mess, the Royal Marines Museum traces the history of this famous Corps from 1664 when marines first entered the service of King Charles II as The Duke of York and Albany's Maritime Regiment of Foot. During the nearly 350 years that have followed, Royal Marines have distinguished themselves across the globe and their deeds are faithfully illustrated in this impressive collection. From the capture of Gibraltar in 1704, through the Napoleonic Wars, the creation of the British Empire and their exploits at sea and on land during both world wars to more recent conflicts in Suez, Borneo, Aden, the Falkland Islands and Afghanistan, well-presented cameos, videos and interactive displays bring the Corps' history to life.

The collection includes items that reflect the worldwide service of the Royal Marines, afloat and ashore in jungle, desert or arctic environments. A comprehensive array of uniforms, weapons and equipment provides an insight into the rigours of life as a ship's marine manning gun turrets or providing boarding parties and the arduous training and daring operations of the Royal Marines Commandos. There is a section devoted to Hannah Snell who, as a young woman, posed as a man and served and fought as a Marine in India in the 1740s. A special room dedicated to the Royal Marines Band Service allows visitors to enjoy the spectacular sight and sound of Beating Retreat by video and contains a Steinway piano from the Royal Yacht Victoria and Albert. The medal room houses one of the most comprehensive collections in the world, including all ten Victoria Crosses won by the Royal Marines .

Opening Hours: Jun–Aug: daily 10am–5pm. Sep–May: daily 10am–4.30pm. Closed Christmas Eve, Christmas Day and Boxing Day

Admission: Adults £5.25, seniors £4.25, students £3.25, children 16 and under £3.25, disabled visitors £3

Facilities: Parking, toilets, shop, tea rooms, picnic area, disabled access, library and research facilities

Directions for Travellers

By car: Via A3(M) from London, M27 from Southampton or A27 from Brighton – follow signs for Southsea and head towards the Seafront, from which the Museum is signposted

By rail: Portsmouth Harbour, Portsmouth and Southsea or Fratton stations – then by bus or taxi

By bus: Buses run from all stations to Eastney plus a moderate walk

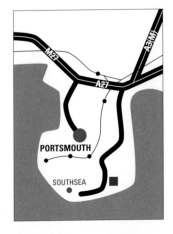

NATIONALS

For a detailed map, go to **www.streetmap.co.uk** and type in the post code of the museum

Portsmouth, Hampshire

ROYAL NAVAL MUSEUM   15

The Royal Naval Museum,
Portsmouth Historic Dockyard,
HM Naval Base (PP66),
Portsmouth PO1 3NH
T. 023 9283 9766 F. 023 9283 8228
www.royalnavalmuseum.org

The history of the Royal Navy dates back over a thousand years to King Alfred's first battle at sea in 882. The Navy has defended Britain from invasion, attacked enemies and eventually established Britain as the dominant world sea power in the 19th century. Today's role involves peacekeeping, fighting piracy and the prevention of drug trafficking. The influence of the Navy can be felt at every level in our society: in our speech, literature, dress, music, character, culture and customs. The history of the Navy is to a remarkable extent the history of Britain.

Located in 18th-century dockyard storehouses facing HMS Victory, the Royal Naval Museum, in Portsmouth's Historic Dockyard, is one of Britain's oldest maritime museums. The Museum's mission is to preserve and present the history of the 'Fleet' – the ships and the men and women who manned them.

Following a £5 million refurbishment programme completed in 1999 it now has four new exhibitions covering the life and times of Horatio Nelson, life in the Sailing Navy, the Battle of Trafalgar and the Story of HMS Victory, together with a gallery devoted to the Navy in the 20th century. Particular highlights include:

Trafalgar!: a multi-media experience. Stand on the gundeck of the Victory and feel what it must have been like to be there on 21 October 1805.

W.L. Wyllie's Panorama: a huge and vivid painting of the battle, with a special sound and light show.

The Nelson Figure and The Nelson Story: our answer to the often-asked question, 'What did Nelson really look like?' and an audio visual presentation of Nelson's life and career.

New in 2007: *Chasing Freedom:* The Royal Navy and the Suppression of Transatlantic Slavery (1807–2007) and Falklands 25: Commemorating the Falklands Conflict of 1982

Opening Hours: Opens daily at 10am (Except 24–26 Dec)
Apr–Oct: Last tickets sold at 4.30pm. Dockyard gates close at 6.00pm.
Nov–Mar: Last tickets sold at 4.00pm. Dockyard gates close at 5.30pm

Admission: Single Attraction Ticket to Royal Naval Museum and HMS Victory: adults £11.50, child/senior £9, family £32. All Inclusive Ticket (one entry to Royal Naval Museum, HMS Victory, HMS Warrior 1860, Mary Rose, Action Stations and Harbour Tours): adults £16, child/senior £13, family £46. Under 5s free. Concessions for disabled visitors and their carers

Facilities: Toilets, shops, restaurant, café. Research and Library facility on request

Directions for Travellers

By road: Follow brown Historic Waterfront signs from M27/J12 and then Historic Dockyard signs

By Coach, Bus, Rail, Ferry: from Gosport or FastCat from Isle of Wight: Portsmouth Harbour Station/ The Hard Interchange are 200 metres from the main entrance to the Dockyard

NATIONALS

Gosport, Hampshire

THE ROYAL NAVY SUBMARINE MUSEUM 16

Haslar Jetty Road, Gosport,
Hants PO12 2AS
T: 02392 510354
F: 02392 511349
www.rnsubmus.co.uk

Director: Cdr Jeff Tall OBE RN
Curator: Mr Bob Mealings AMA

Recently the recipient of two HLF awards to improve its facilities, the Museum represents a century of submarining that has seen huge technological progress. Petrol engines to nuclear reactors; three white mice for air-monitoring to electrolysers and gas scrubbers; periscopes that presented a target upside down when it was astern to non-hull penetrating masts carrying TV cameras and every gismo imaginable; pigeons for long range communications to satcoms; a shared sanitation bucket to flushing loos; a daily starsight to SINS; a single air-driven, 500-yard torpedo, to 16 Trident D5 missiles accompanied by an awesome array of assorted weaponry to meet every requirement.

So the Royal Navy Submarine Museum has a momentous story to tell and stunning collections to support it. It includes three ships of pre-eminent historical importance. Holland 1, the Royal Navy's first submarine, HMS Alliance, of World War II design and X24, the only example of this miniature submarine to have seen service during World War II. It owns a weapon collection that ranges from an early 14in Whitehead Torpedo to a Polaris Missile; a written archive of over 1 million pieces of paper; a photographic archive of over 140,000 images; a library of over 4,000 books; plus a huge collection of medals and personal memorabilia from submariners through the ages who lost one in four of their numbers in World War I and over one in three in World War II. In that process they won 14 VCs and chestfuls of other medals for gallantry.

With its mix of modern multimedia interactives and traditional case-based exhibitions, underpinned by a guided tour of HMS Alliance by a former submariner, the Museum will appeal to all ages. At least three hours should be allowed for the visit.

Opening hours: Apr–Oct: 10am–5.30pm. Oct–Mar: 10am–4.30pm. Closed 24–25 Dec

Admission: Adults £6.50, children and OAPs £5, family ticket (2+4) £15. Disabled, organised youth groups and schools free. Group rates available

Facilities: Free car parking, toilets, café, picnic area, disabled access

Directions for Travellers

Getting here: By car off the M27 at Junction 11 and following the A32. By rail to Portsmouth Harbour and crossing to Gosport by the Gosport Ferry. By waterbus from the railway station, Gunwharf Quays, and the Camber

For a detailed map, go to **www.streetmap.co.uk** and type in the post code of the museum

MAKE A
CAREER JUMP

>> COMBAT

>> ENGINEERING

>> LOGISTICS

>> IT/COMMS

>> HEALTHCARE

>> HR/ADMIN & FINANCE

>> SPECIALIST

>> FURTHER EDUCATION

>> OFFICER

With jobs covering a variety of career groups, great pay (£233 per week during training), sport and adventure, the Army offers an exciting career prospect. Don't just take our word for it; visit your local Army Careers Office and talk to a soldier.

The Army is committed to Equal Opportunities

CALL 08457 300 111 | TXT SOLDIER TO 80010
VISIT ARMYJOBS.MOD.UK

ARMY
BE THE BEST

TERRITORIAL ARMY
BE THE BEST

The Army Museums Ogilby Trust

The Trust is a registered charity founded in 1954 by the late Colonel Robert Ogilby DSO, DL whose personal experiences in two world wars persuaded him that the fighting spirit of the British soldier stemmed from the *esprit de corps* fostered by the Army's regimental structure. This spirit is enshrined in the many regimental and corps museums which seek to inspire and educate their visitors.

Its underlying objectives remain those set by its founder, adapted and developed to encourage a contemporary presentation of military heritage geared to the education of young people by reference to the national curriculum and reflecting the changing needs of regimental and corps museums. Currently the Trust supports museums in the following ways:

- *With the agreement of their trustees, to represent the individual and collective views of regimental and corps museums and to enhance their profile in dealings with the Ministry of Defence, other Government Departments and their agencies.*

- *Through close liaison with the Ministry of Defence, the National Army Museum, the Charity Commissioners and other professional agencies, to track developments in policy and practice and to pass that information to regimental and corps museums through regular conferences, newsletters, strategy papers and visits.*

- *The provision of free legal and specialist advice and assistance with the constitution, structure and registration of existing and projected museums, including the creation of new trusts to embrace the collections of several pre-existing museums.*

- *In conjunction with other agencies to secure for the trustees of regimental and corps museums the best available advice on such professional matters as the protection, conservation, preservation and presentation of their collections and the operation and further development of their museums.*

- *The provision of a website, approved by the Ministry of Defence, as the definitive guide to regimental and corps museums.*

- *Participation in the development of Ministry of Defence policy towards museums to ensure that the interests and concerns of museum trustees are properly represented, thereby ensuring the best possible future for regimental and corps museums.*

The British Army has a rich history that is added to continually as today's regiments carry forward the proud traditions of their forebears. Their museums record this history, linking the past to the present, for the benefit of posterity. The Trust assists such museums with funds, advocacy, information and advice. Its income is derived solely from donations and bequests and it would warmly welcome gifts, legacies or covenants from those who support its views and objectives.

Please help the Trust by:

Making a donation, however, small, which would be most gratefully received by the Director AMOT at this address:

Army Museums Ogilby Trust
58 The Close, Salisbury, Wiltshire
SP1 2EX

Considering a legacy, about which further information and a suitable form of words are available on our website at

www.armymuseums.org.uk

Your generosity will have a direct impact on the preservation of the Nation's military heritage

Index

Part I
Regimental and Corps Museums 9

Part II
Principal National Museums 73

Succession of Titles

Army Museums Ogilby Trust 86

Succession of Titles

CAVALRY

1881	1920/22	1958/60	1970	1992/4
1st Life Guards 2nd Life Guards	Life Guards (1st and 2nd)	Life Guards	Life Guards	Life Guards
Royal Horse Guards (The Blues) 1st (Royal) Dragoons	Royal Horse Guards (The Blues) 1st Royal Dragoons	Royal Horse Guards (The Blues) 1st Royal Dragoons	Blues and Royals (Royal Horse Guards and 1st Dragoons)	Blues and Royals (Royal Horse Guards and 1st Dragoons)
1st (King's) Dragoon Guards 2nd Dragoon Guards (Queen's Bays)	1st King's Dragoon Guards Queen's Bays (2nd Dragoon Guards)	1st Queen's Dragoon Guards	1st Queen's Dragoon Guards	1st Queen's Dragoon Guards
3rd (Prince of Wales's) Dragoon Guards 6th Dragoon Guards (Carabiniers) 2nd Dragoons (Royal Scots Greys)	3rd/6th Dragoon Guards Royal Scots Greys (2nd Dragoons)	3rd Carabiniers (Prince of Wales's Dragoon Guards) Royal Scots Greys	Royal Scots Dragoon Guards (Carabiniers and Greys)	Royal Scots Dragoon Guards (Carabiniers and Greys)
4th (Royal Irish) Dragoon Guards 7th (Princess Royal's) Dragoon Guards 5th (Princess Charlotte of Wales's) Dragoon Guards 6th (Inniskilling) Dragoons	4th/7th Dragoon Guards 5th/6th Dragoons	4th/7th Royal Dragoon Guards 5th Royal Inniskilling Dragoon Guards	4th/7th Royal Dragoon Guards 5th Royal Inniskilling Dragoon Guards	Royal Dragoon Guards
3rd (King's Own) Hussars 7th (Queen's Own) Hussars 4th (Queen's Own) Hussars 8th (King's Royal Irish) Hussars	3rd (King's Own) Hussars 7th (Queen's Own) Hussars 4th (Queen's Own) Hussars 8th (King's Royal Irish) Hussars	Queen's Own Hussars Queen's Royal Irish Hussars	Queen's Own Hussars Queen's Royal Irish Hussars	Queen's Royal Hussars (Queen's Own and Royal Irish)
9th (Queen's Royal) Lancers 12th (Prince of Wales's Royal) Lancers	9th Queen's Royal Lancers 12th Royal Lancers (Prince of Wales's)	9th/12th Royal Lancers (Prince of Wales's)	9th/12th Royal Lancers (Prince of Wales's)	9th/12th Royal Lancers (Prince of Wales's)
10th (Prince of Wales's Own Royal) Hussars 11th (Prince Albert's Own) Hussars 14th (King's) Hussars 20th Hussars	10th Royal Hussars (Prince of Wales's Own) 11th Hussars (Prince Albert's Own) 14th/20th Hussars	10th Royal Hussars (Prince of Wales's Own) 11th Hussars (Prince Albert's Own) 14th/20th King's Hussars	Royal Hussars (Prince of Wales's Own) 14th/20th King's Hussars	King's Royal Hussars

Cavalry

1881	1920/22	1958/60	1970	1992/4
13th Hussars	13th/18th Hussars	13th/18th Royal Hussars	13th/18th Royal Hussars (Queen Mary's Own)	Light Dragoons
18th Hussars				
15th (King's) Hussars	15th/19th Hussars	15th/19th King's Royal Hussars	15th/19th King's Royal Hussars	
19th Hussars				
16th (Queen's Lancers)	16th/5th Lancers	16th/5th Queen's Royal Lancers	16th/5th Queen's Royal Lancers	Queen's Royal Lancers
5th (Royal Irish) Lancers				
17th (Duke of Cambridge's Own) Lancers	17th/21st Lancers	17th/21st Lancers	17th/21st Lancers	
21st Hussars				

INFANTRY

Regt of Foot	1881	1959	1968/70	1992/4	2006/7
	Grenadier Guards	Grenadier Guards	Grenadier Guards	Grenadier Guards	Grenadier Guards
	Coldstream Guards	Coldstream Guards	Coldstream Guards	Coldstream Guards	Coldstream Guards
	Scots Guards	Scots Guards	Scots Guards	Scots Guards	Scots Guards
		Irish Guards	Irish Guards	Irish Guards	Irish Guards
		Welsh Guards	Welsh Guards	Welsh Guards	Welsh Guards
1 / 25	Royal Scots (Lothian Regiment) / The King's Own Borderers	Royal Scots (Royal Regiment) / King's Own Scottish Borderers	Royal Scots (The Royal Regiment) / King's Own Scottish Borderers	Royal Scots (The Royal Regiment) / King's Own Scottish Borderers	Royal Scots Borderers, 1st Bn Royal Regt of Scotland
21 / 71 & 74	Royal Scots Fusiliers / Highland Light Infantry	Royal Highland Fusiliers (Princess Margaret's Own Glasgow and Ayrshire Regiment)	Royal Highland Fusiliers (Princess Margaret's Own Glasgow and Ayrshire Regiment)	Royal Highland Fusiliers (Princess Margaret's Own Glasgow and Ayrshire Regiment)	Royal Highland Fusiliers, 2nd Bn Royal Regt of Scotland
42	Black Watch (Royal Highlanders)	Black Watch (Royal Highland Regiment)	Black Watch (Royal Highland Regiment)	Black Watch (Royal Highland Regiment)	Black Watch, 3rd Bn Royal Regiment of Scotland
72 & 78 / 79 / 75 & 92	Seaforth Highlanders (Ross-shire Buffs, Duke of Albany's Own) / Queen's Own Cameron Highlanders / Gordon Highlanders	Queen's Own Highlanders (Seaforth and Cameron) / Gordon Highlanders	Queen's Own Highlanders (Seaforth and Cameron) / Gordon Highlanders	The Highlanders (Seaforth, Gordons and Camerons)	The Highlanders, 4th Bn Royal Regt of Scotland

Regt of Foot	1881	1959	1968/70	1992/4	2006/7
91 & 93	Princess Louise's (Argyll and Sutherland Highlanders)	Argyll and Sutherland Highlanders (Princess Louise's)	Argyll and Sutherland Highlanders (Princess Louise's)	Argyll and Sutherland Highlanders (Princess Louise's)	Argyll and Sutherland Highlanders, 5th Bn Royal Regt of Scotland
2	Queen's (Royal West Surrey Regiment)	Queen's Royal Surrey Regiment			
31 & 70	East Surrey Regiment				
3	Buffs (East Kent Regiment)	Queen's Own Buffs	Queen's Regiment	Princess of Wales's Royal Regiment	Princess of Wales's Royal Regiment
50 & 97	Queen's Own (Royal West Kent Regiment)				
35 & 107	Royal Sussex Regiment	Royal Sussex Regiment			
57 & 77	Duke of Cambridge's Own (Middlesex Regiment)	Duke of Cambridge's Own (Middlesex Regiment)			
37 & 67	Hampshire Regiment	Royal Hampshire Regiment	Royal Hampshire Regiment		
4	King's Own (Royal Lancaster) Regiment	King's Own Royal Border Regiment	King's Own Royal Border Regiment	King's Own Royal Border Regiment	1st Bn, The Duke of Lancaster's Regiment (King's Lancashire and Border)
34 & 35	Border Regiment				
8	King's (Liverpool Regiment)	King's Regiment (Manchester and Liverpool)	King's Regiment	King's Regiment	
63 & 69	Manchester Regiment				
30 & 59	East Lancashire Regiment	Lancashire Regiment (Prince of Wales's Volunteers)	Queen's Lancashire Regiment	Queen's Lancashire Regiment	2nd Bn, The Duke of Lancaster's Regiment (King's, Lancashire and Border)
40 & 82	Prince of Wales's Volunteers (South Lancashire Regiment)	Loyal Regiment (North Lancashire)			
47 & 81	Loyal North Lancashire Regiment				
5	Northumberland Fusiliers	Royal Northumberland Fusiliers	Royal Regiment of Fusiliers	Royal Regiment of Fusiliers	Royal Regiment of Fusiliers
6	Royal Warwickshire Regiment	Royal Warwickshire Regiment			
7	Royal Fusiliers (City of London Regiment)	Royal Fusiliers (City of London Regiment)			
20	Lancashire Fusiliers	Lancashire Fusiliers			
9	Norfolk Regiment	1st East Anglian Regiment (Royal Norfolk and Suffolk)	Royal Anglian Regiment	Royal Anglian Regiment	Royal Anglian Regiment
12	Suffolk Regiment				
10	Lincolnshire Regiment				
48 & 58	Northamptonshire Regiment	2nd East Anglian Regiment			
16	Bedfordshire Regiment	3rd East Anglian Regiment (16th/44th Foot)			
44 & 56	Essex Regiment				
17	Leicestershire Regiment	Royal Leicestershire Regiment			

Regt of Foot	1881	1959	1968/70	1992/4	2006/7
11	Devonshire Regiment	Devonshire and Dorset Regiment	Devonshire and Dorset Regiment	Devonshire and Dorset Regiment	1st Bn, The Rifles
39 & 54	Dorset Regiment				
28 & 61	Gloucestershire Regiment	Gloucestershire Regiment	Gloucestershire Regiment	Royal Gloucestershire, Berkshire and Wiltshire Regiment	
49 & 66	Princess Charlotte of Wales's (Berkshire Regiment)	Duke of Edinburgh's Royal Regiment	Duke of Edinburgh's Royal Regiment (Berkshire and Wiltshire)		
62 & 99	Duke of Edinburgh's (Wiltshire Regiment)				
13	Prince Albert's (Somerset Light Infantry)	Somerset and Cornwall Light Infantry	1st Bn Light Infantry	The Light Infantry	3rd and 5th Battalions The Rifles
32 & 46	Duke of Cornwall's Light Infantry				
53 & 85	King's Light Infantry (Shropshire Regiment)	King's Shropshire Light Infantry	2nd Bn Light Infantry		
51 & 105	King's Own Light Infantry (South Yorkshire Regiment)	King's Own Yorkshire Light Infantry	3rd Bn Light Infantry		
68 & 106	Durham Light Infantry	Durham Light Infantry	4th Bn Light Infantry		
43 & 52	Oxfordshire and Buckinghamshire Light Infantry	1st Green Jackets (43rd and 52nd)	Royal Green Jackets	Royal Green Jackets	2nd and 4th Battalions The Rifles
60	King's Royal Rifle Corps	2nd Green Jackets, King's Royal Rifle Corps			
	Rifle Brigade (Prince Consort's Own)	3rd Green Jackets The Rifle Brigade			
14	Prince of Wales's Own (West Yorkshire Regiment)	Prince of Wales's Own Regiment of Yorkshire	Prince of Wales's Own Regiment of Yorkshire	Prince of Wales's Own Regiment of Yorkshire	1st Bn, The Yorkshire Regiment
15	East Yorkshire Regiment				
19	Princess of Wales's Own (Yorkshire Regiment)	Green Howards (Alexandra, Princess of Wales's Own Yorkshire Regiment)	Green Howards (Alexandra, Princess of Wales's Own Yorkshire Regiment)	Green Howards (Alexandra, Princess of Wales's Own Yorkshire Regiment)	2nd Bn The Yorkshire Regiment
33 & 76	Duke of Wellington's Regiment (West Riding Regiment)	Duke of Wellington's Regiment (West Riding Regiment)	Duke of Wellington's Regiment (West Riding Regiment)	Duke of Wellington's Regiment (West Riding Regiment)	3rd Bn The Yorkshire Regiment
22	Cheshire Regiment	Cheshire Regiment	Cheshire Regiment	Cheshire Regiment	1st Bn, The Mercian Regiment (Cheshire)
29 & 36	Worcestershire Regiment	Worcestershire Regiment	Worcestershire and Sherwood Foresters Regiment (29th/45th Foot)	Worcestershire and Sherwood Foresters	2nd Bn The Mercian Regiment (Worcesters and Foresters)
45 & 95	Sherwood Foresters (Derbyshire Regiment)	Sherwood Foresters (Nottinghamshire and Derbyshire Regiment)			
38 & 80	South Staffordshire Regiment	Staffordshire Regiment (The Prince of Wales's)	Staffordshire Regiment (The Prince of Wales's)	Staffordshire Regiment (The Prince of Wales's)	3rd Bn, The Mercian Regiment (Staffords)
64 & 98	Prince of Wales's (North Staffordshire Regiment)				

Regt of Foot	1881	1959	1968/72	1992/4	2006/7
23	Royal Welsh Fusiliers	Royal Welsh Fusiliers	Royal Welsh Fusiliers	Royal Welch Fusiliers	1st Bn The Royal Welsh (Royal Welch Fusiliers)
24	South Wales Borderers	South Wales Borderers	Royal Regiment of Wales (24th/41st Foot)	Royal Regiment of Wales (24th/41st Foot)	2nd Bn The Royal Welsh The Royal Regiment of Wales
41 & 69	Welsh Regiment	Welch Regiment			
27 & 108	Royal Inniskilling Fusiliers	Royal Inniskilling Fusiliers	Royal Irish Rangers (27th (Inniskilling) 83rd and 87th)	Royal Irish Regiment (on amalgamation with the Ulster Defence Regiment)	Royal Irish Regiment
83 & 86	Royal Ulster Rifles	Royal Ulster Rifles			
87 & 89	Princess Victoria's Royal Irish Fusiliers	Royal Irish Fusiliers (Princess Victoria's)			
	Parachute Regiment	Parachute Regiment	Parachute Regiment	Parachute Regiment	Parachute Regiment
18	Royal Irish Regiment	Disbanded 1922			
26 & 90	Cameronians (Scottish Rifles)	Disbanded 1968			
64 & 84	York and Lancaster Regiment	Suspended animation 1968			
88 & 94	Connaught Rangers	Disbanded 1922			
100 & 109	Prince of Wales's Leinster Regiment (Royal Canadians)	Disbanded 1922			
101 & 104	Royal Munster Fusiliers	Disbanded 1922			
102 & 103	Royal Dublin Fusiliers	Disbanded 1922			
	2nd King Edward VII's Own Gurkha Rifles (The Sirmoor Rifles)	2nd King Edward VII's Own Gurkha Rifles (The Sirmoor Rifles)	2nd King Edward VII's Own Gurkha Rifles (The Sirmoor Rifles)	Royal Gurkha Rifles	Royal Gurkha Rifles
	6th Gurkha Rifles	6th Queen Elizabeth's Own Gurkha Rifles	6th Queen Elizabeth's Own Gurkha Rifles		
	7th Gurkha Rifles	7th Duke of Edinburgh's Own Gurkha Rifles	7th Duke of Edinburgh's Own Gurkha Rifles		
	10th Gurkha Rifles	10th Princess Mary's Own Gurkha Rifles	10th Princess Mary's Own Gurkha Rifles		
	Special Air Service Regiment	Special Air Service Regiment	Special Air Service Regiment	Special Air Service Regiment	Special Air Service Regiment

ORDER ONLINE AND SAVE

Sandhurst:
A Tradition of Leadership

Christopher Pugsley and Angela Holdsworth

Hardback / 192 pages / 305 x 254 mm
Over 300 colour and mono illustrations

The Royal Military Academy at Sandhurst, England, has a national and international reputation for instilling the arts and disciplines of leadership in tomorrow's commanders. It is the spiritual home of the officer corps of the British Army, and equally evokes a sense of belonging in thousands of overseas officers, who trained here.

But what makes it so extraordinary? What makes it tick? Is it the place, its buildings, history, heritage and ethos, its training for leadership? Or is it the people, the Captains, the NCO's and the military staff, the academics and all those who work there?

This stunningly illustrated 192 page hardback book – the first authorised comprehensive full-colour publication on the subject – explores and explains what makes Sandhurst so special. Beautifully designed and produced with compelling new photography, specially commissioned for the book, this is a vibrant portrait of a uniquely British centre of excellence that continues to wield an unprecedented degree of cultural influence throughout the world.

"This book …sets out, by fine design and lavish illustration, to capture both the Sandhurst scene and its elusive but powerful ethos, which has planted the highest standards of leadership not only in our own army but in many others around the world."
Sir John Keegan, Daily Telegraph

"This beautifully produced book encapsulates the Sandhurst experience beautifully … The stunning photographs and illustrations serve to underline the pain, passion and pride."
Rupert Uloth, Country Life

"… not just a history; it is the living history of the RMAS told through the anecdotes of those who have passed off its famous parade square …"
Soldier Magazine

"I highly recommend this book for any military enthusiast."
The Officer Magazine

Special direct discount price when you order online (see below)

Trade orders are available via Marston Book Services – www.marston.co.uk

Visit **www.tmiltd.com** to order securely online or call
Third Millennium Information on +44 (0)20 7336 0144

ORDER ONLINE AND SAVE

Excellence in Action:
Portrait of the Guards

General Editor: Rupert Uloth

Hardback / 192 pages / 305 x 254 mm
Over 200 colour and mono illustrations

The story of the seven regiments which compose the Household Division, commonly referred to as the Guards, has been often told, individually and jointly. To the world at large, the image of the Guards has been coloured by their ceremonial duties as the regiments dedicated to the protection of the sovereign – whether on duty at Buckingham Palace and Horse Guards, or at great national occasions such as The Queen's Birthday Parade, which the public know as the Trooping of the Colour.

Yet in the 21st century the Guards have never been more active and engaged in their role as highly effective operational military units, whether in Bosnia, Iraq or, more recently, Afghanistan. *Excellence in Action* is a new, richly illustrated publication which offers a true, wide-ranging colour portrait of the Household Division which reflects the traditions of excellence of the individual formations in the context of today's role as an elite fighting force.

FROM THE MAJOR GENERAL

I am delighted to commend to you this new publication offering a detailed and far-reaching, highly illustrated account of the Household Division today, encompassing the traditions, values and aspirations that have long made the Guards regiments a watchword for excellence in peace and war.

SIR Roberts.

SEBASTIAN ROBERTS

The book will be published in November 2007 but is available to order online in advance of publication at a discount on the recommended retail price.

Visit **www.tmiltd.com** to order securely online or call
Third Millennium Information on +44 (0)20 7336 0144